The Validation of Scientific Theories

edited, with an introduction, by

PHILIPP G. FRANK

THE

VALIDATION
OF SCIENTIFIC
THEORIES

COLLIER BOOKS
NEW YORK, N.Y.

This Collier Books edition is published
by arrangement with The Beacon Press.

Collier Books is a division of the Crowell-
Collier Publishing Company

First Collier Books Edition 1961

The papers published here were first presented at the annual meeting of the American Association for the Advancement of Science in
Boston, Massachusetts, December 1953, and sponsored by the Insti
tute for the Unity of Science, the Philosophy of Science Association
and Section L (History and Philosophy of Science) of AAAS; co
sponsored by the National Science Foundation and the American
Academy of Arts and Sciences. These articles were published in the
September, October, November 1954, and January and February
1955 issues of *The Scientific Monthly*, and permission to reproduce
any of the papers or parts therefrom must be obtained from *The
Scientific Monthly*.

Hecho en los E.E.U.U.
Printed in the United States of America

Contents

Introduction

Among the disparaging judgments about science that have been uttered since the rise of modern science about 1700 until our own century there has been the assertion that science does not give us the "truth" about the universe but only an abstract model which may be useful as a "working hypothesis." This assertion has become popular in our own period in connection with the complaint that the emphasis upon science in our educational system is responsible for the decline of belief in spiritual and moral values and, perhaps, in human values altogether. Quite a few educators have urged that more emphasis should be given to the studies of "humanities" like philosophy, literature, history, and religion. On the other hand, there has been, in this country, grave concern about the declining number of science students, which leads, in turn, to a scarcity of science teachers and so on, in a spiral. The increasing unpopularity of science as a chosen field of the high school curriculum has also been traced back to the alleged lack of human values in the sciences. Quite a few leading educators in the field of science have surmised that the social and family background of high school students have imbued them with a certain aversion against a field from which so little about human values or about how to live can be learnt. Since, anyway, science, and particularly, physical science, is "hard" to learn, a certain drift away from science is understandable.

In order to obtain a basis from which one can pronounce sound judgment about this situation, one should put the question: In what sense does science search for the "truth" about the universe? This "truth" certainly does not consist of "facts" but of general hypotheses or theories. What we call "facts" in the strictly empirical sense, without any admixture of theory, are, in the last analysis, sense impressions between which no connection is given. Hence, the question of what we have to regard as the "truth" about the universe has to be formulated rather as follows: "What are the criteria under which we accept a hypothesis or a theory?" If we put this or a similar question, we shall see soon that these criteria will contain, to a certain extent, the psychological and sociological characteristics of the scientist, because they are relevant for the acceptance of any doctrine. In other words, the validation of "theories" cannot be separated neatly from the values which the scientist accepts. This is true in all fields of science, over the whole spectrum ranging from geometry and mechanics to psychoanalysis.

Since about 1930, the "Unity of Science" movement has attempted to study the traits which are common to all scientific theories. The "Institute for the Unity of Science," in Boston, has organized local, national, and international meetings in which the results of these studies have been presented and discussed by cooperation with scientists and philosophers of various lines and specialties. In the year 1953, a plan was developed to come to grips with the central problem by organizing a special conference on the "Validation of Scientific Theories." In cooperation with the American Academy of Arts and Sciences, in Boston, and under the sponsorship of the National Science Foundation, in Washington, the conference was organized in the Christmas vacation, 1953, as a part of the meeting held by the American Association for the Advancement of Science.

The conference started by discussing the reasons for the acceptance of scientific theories in general. This issue was not treated from the logical viewpoint only. Besides the roles of deductive and inductive logic, the "pragmatic" reasons of acceptance were stressed. The reasons for acceptance depend upon the purpose whch the theory has to serve. The participants were P. Frank as scientist, and the philosophers W. Churchman and R. Rudner. As an illustration to this pragmatic, the sociologist H. Moore presented the situation in the Soviet Union, where the acceptance of theories is, more than in other countries, dependent upon its fitness to serve the goals of the government and the ruling party.

From the viewpoint of the physical or biological scientist the acceptance of a theory depends greatly upon its fitness to be put to an experimental test. This is, obviously, only possible if one can derive from the principles of the theory statements about observable phenomena. In the physical sciences, an observation is carried out by a measurement that consists in a physical operation. Since this method has been successful the opinion that all scientific theories should be tested in a similar way has gained ground. This would mean that every testable theory has to contain the description of the operations by which it can be tested. If a theory fits this requirement, it has, according to P. W. Bridgman, an "operational meaning." This requirement itself has been known under the name of "operationalism." Obviously, it is difficult to formulate this criterion in a completely satisfactory way. Since, on the other hand, it is the central point in making theories testable, the conference devoted one seminar to the "Present State of Operationalism." Prominent physicists, logicians, and philosophers participated in the discussion. Besides P. W. Bridgman, the speakers were: H. Margenau, G. Bergmann, C. Hempel, R. B. Lindsay, R. J. Seeger.

The "Theory of Theories" which deals with the logical structure of scientific theories has been established mainly according to the example of the physical sciences. To this point, the conference had mostly followed these lines. Quite a few people have doubted whether in fields which are very remote from the physical sciences the logical structure and the rules for acceptance may be very different from what we have learnt from the example of the physical sciences. In order to get a certain judgment about the similarity and dissimilarities of theories in different fields, the conference treated fields that are as far from the physical sciences as one can imagine. In a special session Freud's psychoanalysis was discussed by a group of well-known psychologists: Else Frenkel-Brunswik, B. F. Skinner, J. Richfield, M. Scriven. The purpose of this symposium was to explore the role of psychoanalysis as a science.

According to the widely held opinion the deepest gap within the sciences is the gap between the physical sciences and the life sciences. It seems to a great number of scientists and philosophers that the criteria for the acceptance of theories on both sides of this gap are very different and even heterogeneous. In order to explore this situation, the conference devoted one session to the topic: "Organism and Machine." The problem was attacked by a group of speakers who started from very different backgrounds. The psychologist W. Koehler, one of the founders of "Gestaltpsychology," spoke from a general philosophical viewpoint; N. Rashevski, the founder of mathematical biophysics, along the lines of exact sciences; and the neurobiologist W. S. McCulloch from the viewpoint of cybernetics, flavored with poetry and irony, as in his words: "Cybernetics has helped to pull down the wall between the great world of physics and the ghetto of the mind."

In order to study the pragmatic aspects of scientific theories by concrete examples the last session was devoted to "Science as a Social and Historical Phenomenon." The participants were, on the one hand, historians and philosophers of science: H. Guerlac, A. Koyré, R. S. Cohen, and, on the other hand, the Harvard psychologist, E. G. Boring.

The chairmen and organizers of the five sessions were: R. J. Seeger (Washington), H. Margenau (Yale), H. Feigl (Minnesota), G. Wald (Harvard), G. Holton (Harvard).

The conference was held in Boston simultaneously with the meeting of the American Association for the Advancement of Science at which several thousands of specialists from all fields of the sciences participated. It has been frequently said that the representatives of the "special sciences" (physics, biology, geology, etc.) were not interested in the general questions which were discussed in the conference; quite a few "specialists" take even a rather disparaging attitude toward "philosophy," as the dealing with general problems of science is often called. But observing the conference and the huge meeting of specialists, one could not help noting how great the actual number of "specialists" was who were flocking into the conference. Since one of its goals had been to stimulate the interest for interscience work, for building of bridges between the special sciences, for a "unity of science," this effect upon the members of the American Association for the Advancement of Science was certainly encouraging. By publishing the papers, the organizers of the conference hope to make this success a broader one.

PHILIPP G. FRANK

Chapter 1

Acceptance of Scientific Theories

The Variety of Reasons for the Acceptance of Scientific Theories

by Philipp G. Frank

AMONG SCIENTISTS it is taken for granted that a theory "should be" accepted if and only if it is "true"; to be true means in this context to be in agreement with the observable facts that can be logically derived from the theory. Every influence of moral, religious, or political considerations upon the acceptance of a theory is regarded as "illegitimate" by the so-called "community of scientists." This view certainly has had a highly salutary effect upon the evolution of science as a human activity. It tells the truth—but not the whole truth. It has never happened that all the conclusions drawn from a theory have agreed with the observable facts. The scientific community has accepted theories only when a vast number of facts has been derived from few and simple principles. A familiar example is the derivation of the immensely complex motions of celestial bodies from the simple Newtonian formula of gravitation, or the large variety of electromagnetic phenomena from Maxwell's field equations.

If we restrict our attention to the two criterions that are called "agreement with observations" and "simplicity," we remain completely within the domain of activities that are cultivated and approved by the community of scientists. But, if we have to choose a certain theory for acceptance, we do not know what respective weight should be attributed to these two criterions. There is obviously no theory that agrees with *all* observations and no theory that has "perfect" simplicity. Therefore, in every individual case, one has to make a choice of a theory by a compromise between both criterions. However, when we try to specify the degree of "simplicity" in different theories, we soon notice that attempts of this kind lead us far beyond the limits of physical science. Everybody would agree that a linear function is simpler than a function of the second or higher degree; everybody would also admit that a circle is simpler than an ellipse. For this

reason, physics is filled with laws that express proportion-
ality, such as Hooke's law in elasticity or Ohm's law in electrodynamics. In all these cases, there is no doubt that a non-
linear relationship would describe the facts in a more accurate way, but one tries to get along with a linear law as
much as possible.

There was a time when, in physics, laws that could be expressed without using differential calculus were preferred,
and in the long struggle between the corpuscular and the
wave theories of light, the argument was rife that the corpuscular theory was mathematically simpler, while the wave
theory required the solution of boundary problems of partial
differential equations, a highly complex matter. We note
that even a purely mathematical estimation of simplicity
depends upon the state of culture of a certain period. People
who have grown up in a mathematical atmosphere—that is,
saturated with ideas about invariants—will find that Einstein's theory of gravitation is of incredible beauty and simplicity; but to people for whom ordinary calculus is the center of interest, Einstein's theory will be of immense complexity, and this low degree of simplicity will not be compensated
by a great number of observed facts.

However, the situation becomes much more complex, if
we mean by *simplicity* not only simplicity of the mathematical scheme but also simplicity of the whole discourse by
which the theory is formulated. We may start from the most
familiar instance, the decision between the Copernican
(heliocentric) and the Ptolemaic (geocentric) theories.
Both parties, the Roman Church and the followers of Copernicus, agreed that Copernicus' system, from the purely
mathematical angle, was simpler than Ptolemy's. In the first
one, the orbits of planets were plotted as a system of con-
centric circles with the sun as center, whereas in the geocentric system, the planetary orbits were sequences of loops.
The observed facts covered by these systems were approxi-
mately the same ones. The criterions of acceptance that are
applied in the community of scientists today are, according
to the usual way of speaking, in agreement with observed
facts and mathematical simplicity. According to them, the
Copernican system had to be accepted unhesitatingly. Since
this acceptance did not happen before a long period of
doubt, we see clearly that the criterions "agreement with observed facts" and "mathematical simplicity" were not the

only criterions that were considered as reasons for the acceptance of a theory.

As a matter of fact, there were three types of reasons against the acceptance of the Copernican theory that remained unchallenged at the time when all "scientific" reasons were in favor of that theory. First, there was the incompatibility of the Copernican system with the traditional interpretation of the Bible. Second, there was the disagreement between the Copernican system and the prevailing philosophy of that period, the philosophy of Aristotle as it was interpreted by the Catholic schoolmen. Third, there was the objection that the mobility of the earth, as a real physical fact, is incompatible with the common-sense interpretation of nature. Let us consider these three types of reasons more closely. In the Book of Joshua this leader prays to God to stop the sun in its motion in order to prolong the day and to enable the people of Israel to win a decisive victory. God indeed "stopped the sun." If interpreted verbally, according to the usage of words in our daily language, this means that the sun is moving, in flagrant contradiction with the Copernican theory. One could, of course, give a more sophisticated interpretation and say that "God stopped the sun" means that he stopped it in its motion relative to the earth. This is no longer contradictory to the Copernican system. But now the question arises: Should we adopt a simple mathematical description and a complicated, rather "unnatural" interpretation of the Bible or a more complicated mathematical description (motion in loops) and a simple "natural" interpretation of the biblical text? The decision certainly cannot be achieved by any argument taken from physical science.

If one believes that all questions raised by science must be solved by the "methods" of this special science, one must say: Every astronomer who lived in the period between Copernicus and Galileo was "free" to accept either the Copernican or the Ptolemaic doctrine; he could make an "arbitrary" decision. However, the situation is quite different if one takes into consideration that physical science is only a part of science in general. Building up astronomical theories is a particular act of human behavior. If we consider human behavior in general, we look at physical science as a part of a much more general endeavor that embraces also psychology and sociology. It is called by some authors "behavioristics."

From this more general angle, the effect of a simplification in the mathematical formula and the simplification in biblical interpretation are quite comparable with each other. There is meaning in asking by which act the happiness of human individuals and groups is more favorably influenced. This means that, from the viewpoint of a general science of human behavior, the decision between the Copernican and Ptolemaic systems was never a matter of arbitrary decision.

The compatibility of a physical theory with a certain interpretation of the Bible is a special case of a much more general criterion: the compatibility of a physical theory with theories that have been advanced to account for observable phenomena outside the domain of physical science. The most important reason for the acceptance of a theory beyond the "scientific criterions" in the narrower sense (agreement with observation and simplicity of the mathematical pattern) is the fitness of a theory to be generalized, to be the basis of a new theory that does not logically follow from the original one, and to allow prediction of more observable facts. This property is often called the "dynamical" character or the "fertility" of a theory. In this sense, the Copernican theory is much superior to the geocentric one. Newtonian laws of motion have a simple form only if the sun is taken as a system of reference and not the earth. But the decision in favor of the Copernican theory on this basis could be made only when Newton's laws came into existence. This act requires, however, creative imagination or, to speak more flippantly, a happy guessing that leads far beyond the Copernican and Ptolemaic systems.

However, long before the "dynamical" character of the Copernican system was recognized, the objection was raised that the system was incompatible with "the general laws of motion" that could be derived from principles regarded as "immediately intelligible" or, in other words, "self-evident" without physical experiment or observations. From such "self-evident" principles there followed, for example, the physical law that only celestial bodies (like sun or moon) moved "naturally" in circular orbits, while terrestrial bodies (like our earth) moved naturally along straight lines as a falling stone does. Copernicus' theory of a "motion of the earth in a circular orbit" was, therefore, incompatible with "self-evident laws of nature."

Medieval scientists were faced with the alternatives:

Should they accept the Copernican theory with its simple mathematical formulas and drop the self-evident laws of motion, or should they accept the complicated mathematics of the Ptolemaic system along with the intelligible and self-evident general laws of motion. Acceptance of Copernicus' theory would imply dropping the laws of motion that had been regarded as self-evident and looking for radically new laws. This would also mean dropping the contention that a physical law can be derived from "intelligible principles. "Again, from the viewpoint of physical science, this decision cannot be made. Although an arbitrary decision may seem to be required, if one looks at the situation from the viewpoint of human behavior it is clear that the decision, by which the derivation of physical laws from self-evident principles is abandoned, would alter the situation of man in the world fundamentally. For example, an important argument for the existence of spiritual beings would lose its validity. Thus, social science had to decide whether the life of man would become happier or unhappier by the acceptance of the Copernican system.

The objections to this system, on the basis of self-evident principles, have also been formulated in a way that looks quite different but may eventually, when the chips are down, not be so very different. Francis Bacon, the most conspicuous adversary of Aristotelianism in the period of Galileo, fought the acceptance of the Copernican theory on the basis of common-sense experience. He took it for granted that the principles of science should be as analogous as possible to the experience of our daily life. Then, the principles could be presented in the language that has been shaped for the purpose of describing, in the most convenient way, the experience of our daily existence—the language that everyone has learned as a child and that is called "common-sense language." From this daily experience, we have learned that the behavior of the sun and the planets is very different from that of the earth. While the earth does not emit any light, the sun and the planets are brilliant; while every earthly object that becomes separated from the main body will tend to fall back toward the center and stop there, the celestial objects undergo circular motion eternally around the center.

To separate the sun from the company of the planets and put the earth among these brilliant and mobile creatures, as

Copernicus suggested, would have been not only unnatura
but a serious violation of the rule to keep the principles o
science as close to common sense as possible. We see by thi
example that one of the reasons for the acceptance of a
theory has frequently been the compatibility of this theory
with daily life experience or, in other words, the possibilit
of expressing the theory in common-sense language. Here
is, of course, the source of another conflict between the
"scientific" reasons for the acceptance of a theory and othe
requirements that are not "scientific" in the narrower sense
Francis Bacon rejected the Copernican system because i
was not compatible with common sense.

In the eighteenth and nineteenth centuries, Newton's
mechanics not only had become compatible with commo
sense but had even been identified with common-sense judgment. As a result, in twentieth century physics, the theory o
relativity and the quantum theory were regarded by many
as incompatible with common sense. These theories were
regarded as "absurd" or, at least, "unnatural." Lenard in
Germany, Bouasse in France, O'Rahilly in Ireland, and
Timiryaseff in Russia rejected the theory of relativity, as
Francis Bacon had rejected the Copernican system. Looking at the historical record, we notice that the requirement
of compatibility with common sense and the rejection o
"unnatural theories" have been advocated with a highly
emotional undertone, and it is reasonable to raise the question: What was the source of heat in those fights against
new and absurd theories? Surveying these battles, we easily
find one common feature, the apprehension that a disagreement with common sense may deprive scientific theories of
their value as incentives for a desirable human behavior. In
other words, by becoming incompatible with common sense,
scientific theories lose their fitness to support desirable attitudes in the domain of ethics, politics, and religion.

Examples are abundant from all periods of theory-building. According to an old theory that was prevalent in ancient
Greece and was accepted by such men as Plato and Aristotle,
the sun, planets, and other celestial bodies were made of a
material that was completely different from the material of
which our earth consists. The great gap between the celestial
and the terrestrial bodies was regarded as required by our
common-sense experience. There were men—for example,
the followers of Epicurus—who rejected this view and as-

sumed that all bodies in the universe, earth and stars, consist of the same material. Nevertheless, many educators and political leaders were afraid that denial of the exceptional status of the celestial bodies in physical science would make it more difficult to teach the belief in the existence of spiritual beings as distinct from material bodies; and since it was their general conviction that the belief in spiritual beings is a powerful instrument to bring about a desirable conduct among citizens, a physical theory that supported this belief seemed to be highly desirable.

Plato, in his famous book *Laws,* suggested that people in his ideal state who taught the "materialistic" doctrine about the constitution of sun and stars should be jailed. He even suggested that people who knew about teachers of that theory and did not report them to the authorities should also be jailed. We learn from this ancient example how scientific theories have served as instruments of indoctrination. Obviously, fitness to support a desirable conduct of citizens or, briefly, to support moral behavior, has served through the ages as a reason for acceptance of a theory. When the "scientific criterions" did not uniquely determine a theory, its fitness to support moral or political indoctrination became an important factor for its acceptance. It is important to learn that the interpretation of a scientific theory as a support of moral rules is not a rare case but has played a role in all periods of history.

This role probably can be traced back to a fact that is well known to modern students of anthropology and sociology. The conduct of man has always been shaped according to the example of an ideal society; on the other hand, this ideal has been represented by the "behavior" of the universe, which is, in turn, determined by the laws of nature, in particular, by the physical laws. In this sense, the physical laws have always been interpreted as examples for the conduct of man or, briefly speaking, as moral laws. Ralph Waldo Emerson wrote in his essay *Nature* that "the laws of physics are also the laws of ethics." He used as an example the law of the lever, according to which "the smallest weight may be made to life the greatest, the difference of weight being compensated by time."

We see the connection of the laws of desirable human conduct with the physical laws of the universe when we glance at the Book of Genesis. The first chapter presents a physical theory about the creation of the world. But the story of the creation serves also as an example for the moral behavior of men; for instance, because the creation took 7 days, we all feel obliged to rest on each seventh day. Perhaps the history of the Great Flood is even more instructive. When the Flood abated, God established a Covenant with the human race: "Never again shall all flesh be cut off by the waters of a flood; neither shall there any more be a flood to destroy the earth." As a sign of the Covenant the rainbow appeared: "When I bring clouds over the earth and the bow is seen in the clouds, I will remember the Covenant which is between me and you, and the waters shall never again become a flood to destroy all flesh." If we read the biblical text carefully, we understand that what God actually pledged was to maintain, without exception, the validity of the physical laws or, in other words, of the causal law. God pledged: "While the earth remains, seedtime and harvest, cold and heat, summer and winter, day and night shall not cease."

All the physical laws, including the law of causality, were given to mankind as a reward for moral behavior and can be canceled if mankind does not behave well. So even the belief in the validity of causal laws in the physical world has supported the belief in God as the supreme moral authority who would punish every departure from moral behavior by abolishing causality. We have seen that Epicurean physics and Copernican astronomy were rejected on moral grounds. We know that Newton's physics was accepted as supporting the belief in a God who was an extremely able engineer and who created the world as a machine that performed its motions according to his plans. Even the generalization of Newtonian science that was advanced by 18th century materialism claimed to serve as a support for the moral behavior of man. In his famous book *Man a Machine,* which has often been called an "infamous book," La Mettrie stresses the point that by regarding men, animals, and planets as beings of the same kind, man is taught to regard them all as his brothers and to treat them kindly.

It would be a great mistake to believe that this situation has changed in the nineteenth and twentieth centuries. A great many authors have rejected the biological theory that organisms have arisen from inanimate matter (spontaneous generation), because such a theory would weaken the belief in the dignity of man and in the existence of a soul and would, therefore, be harmful to moral conduct. In twentieth century physics, we have observed that Einstein's theory of relativity has been interpreted as advocating an "idealistic" philosophy, which, in turn, would be useful as a support of moral conduct. Similarly, the quantum theory is interpreted as supporting a weakening of mechanical determinism and, along with it, the introduction of "indeterminism" into physics. In turn, a great many educators, theologians, and politicians have enthusiastically acclaimed this "new physics" as providing a strong argument for the acceptance of "indeterminism" as a basic principle of science.

The special mechanism by which social powers bring about a tendency to accept or reject a certain theory depends upon the structure of the society within which the scientist operates. It may vary from a mild influence on the scientist by friendly reviews in political or educational dailies to promotion of his book as a best seller, to ostracism as an author and as a person, to loss of his job, or, under some social circumstances, even to imprisonment, torture, and execution. The honest scientist who works hard in his laboratory or computation-room would obviously be inclined to say that all this is nonsense—that his energy should be directed toward finding out whether, say, a certain theory is "true" and that he "should not" pay any attention to the fitness of a theory to serve as an instrument in the fight for educational or political goals. This is certainly the way in which the situation presents itself to most active scientists. However, scientists are also human beings and are definitely inclined toward some moral, religious, or political creed. Those who deny emphatically that there is any connection between scientific theories and religious or political creeds believe in these creeds on the basis of indoctrination that has been provided by organizations such as churches or political parties. This attitude leads to the conception of a "double truth" that is not only logically confusing but morally dangerous. It can lead to the practice of serving God on Sunday and the devil on weekdays.

The conviction that science is independent of all moral and political influences arises when we regard science either as a collective of facts or as a picture of objective reality. But today, everyone who has attentively studied the logic of science will know that science actually is an instrument that serves the purpose of connecting present events with future events and deliberately utilizes this knowledge to shape future physical events as they are desired. This instrument consists of a system of propositions—principles—and the operational definitions of their terms. These propositions certainly cannot be derived from the facts of our experience and are not uniquely determined by these facts. Rather they are hypotheses from which the facts can be logically derived. If the principles or hypotheses are not determined by the physical facts, by what are they determined? We have learned by now that, besides the agreement with observed facts, there are other reasons for the acceptance of a theory: simplicity, agreement with common sense, fitness for supporting a desirable human conduct, and so forth. All these factors participate in the making of a scientific theory. We remember, however, that according to the opinion of the majority of active scientists, these extrascientific factors "should not" have any influence on the acceptance of a scientific theory. But who has claimed and who can claim that they "should not"?

This firm conviction of the scientists comes from the philosophy that they have absorbed since their early childhood. The theories that are built up by "scientific" methods, in the narrower sense, are "pictures" of physical reality. Presumably they tell us the "truth" about the world. If a theory built up exclusively on the ground of its agreement with observable facts tells the "truth" about the world, it would be nonsense to assume seriously that a scientific theory can be influenced by moral or political reasons. However, we learned that "agreement with observed facts" does not single out one individual theory. We never have one theory that is in full agreement but several theories that are in partial agreement, and we have to determine the final theory by a compromise. The final theory has to be in fair agreement with observations and also has to be sufficiently simple to be usable. If we consider this point, it is obvious that such a theory cannot be "the truth." In modern science a theory is regarded as an instrument that serves toward some definite purpose. It has to be helpful in predicting future observable facts on the basis of facts that have been observed in the past and the present. It should also be helpful in the construction of machines and devices that can save us time and labor. A scientific theory is, in a sense, a tool that produces other tools according to a practical scheme.

In the same way that we enjoy the beauty and elegance of an airplane, we also enjoy the "elegance" of the theory that makes the construction of the plane possible. In speaking about any actual machine, it is meaningless to ask whether the machine is "true" in the sense of its being "perfect." We can ask only whether it is "good" or sufficiently "perfect" for a certain purpose. If we require speed as our purpose, the "perfect" airplane will differ from one that is "perfect" for the purpose of endurance. The result will be different again if we choose safety, or fun, or convenience for reading and sleeping as our purpose. It is impossible to design an airplane that fulfills all these purposes in a maximal way. We have to make some compromises. But then, there is the question: Which is more important, speed or safety, or fun or endurance? These questions cannot be answered by any agreement taken from physical science. From the viewpoint of "science proper" the purpose is arbitrary, and science can teach us only how to construct a plane that will achieve a specified speed with a specified degree of safety. There will be a debate, according to moral, political, and even religious lines, by which it will be determined how to produce the compromise. The policy-making authorities are, from the logical viewpoint, "free" to make their choice of which type of plane should be put into production. However, if we look at the situation from the viewpoint of a unified science that includes both physical and social science, we shall understand how the compromise between speed and safety, between fun and endurance is determined by the social conditions that produce the conditioned reflexes of the policymakers. The conditioning may be achieved, for example, by letters written to congressmen. As a matter of fact, the building of a scientific theory is not essentially different from the building of an airplane.

If we look for an answer to the question of whether a certain theory, say the Copernican system or the theory of relativity, is perfect or true, we have to ask the preliminary questions: What purpose is the theory to serve? Is it only the purely technical purpose of predicting observable facts? Or is it to obtain a simple and elegant theory that allows us to derive a great many facts from simple principles? We choose the theory according to our purpose. For some groups, the main purpose of a theory may be to serve as a support in teaching a desirable way of life or to discourage an undesirable way of life. Then, we would prefer theories that give a rather clumsy picture of observed facts, provided that we can get from the theory a broad view of the universe in which man plays the role that we desire to give him. If we wish to speak in a more brief and general way, we may distinguish just two purposes of a theory: the usage for the construction of devices (technological purpose) and the usage for guiding human conduct (sociological purpose).

The actual acceptance of theories by man has always been a compromise between the technological and the sociological usage of science. Human conduct has been influenced directly by the latter, by supporting specific religious or political creeds, while the technological influence has been rather indirect. Technological changes have to produce social changes that manifest themselves in changing human conduct. Everybody knows of the Industrial Revolution of the nineteenth century and the accompanying changes in human life from a rural into an urban pattern. Probably the rise of atomic power will produce analogous changes in man's way of life.

The conflict between the technological and the sociological aims of science is the central factor in the history of science as a human enterprise. If thoroughly investigated, it will throw light upon a factor that some thinkers, Marxist as well as religious thinkers, regard as responsible for the social crisis of our time: the backwardness of social progress compared with technological progress. To cure this illness of our time, an English bishop recommended, some years ago, the establishment of a "truce" in the advancement in technology, in order to give social progress some time to keep up with technological advancement. We have seen examples of this conflict in Plato's indictment of astrophysical theories that could be used as a support of "materialism." We note the same purpose in the fight against the Copernican system and, in our own century, against the Darwinian theory of evolution, against Mendel's laws of heredity, and so forth.

A great many scientists and educators believe that such a conflict no longer exists in our time, because now it is completely resolved by "the scientific method," which theory is the only valid one. This opinion is certainly wrong if we consider theories of high generality. In twentieth century physics, we note clearly that a formulation of the general principles of subatomic physics (quantum theory) is accepted or rejected according to whether we believe that introduction of "indeterminism" into physics gives comfort to desirable ethical postulates or not. Some educators and politicians have been firmly convinced that the belief in "free will" is necessary for ethics and that "free will" is not compatible with Newtonian physics but is compatible with quantum physics. The situation in biology is similar. If we consider the attitude of biologists toward the question whether living organisms have developed from inanimate matter, we shall find that the conflict between the technological and the sociological purposes of theories is in full bloom. Some prominent biologists say that the existence of "spontaneous generation" is highly probable, while others of equal prominence claim that it is highly improbable. If we investigate the reasons for these conflicting attitudes, we shall easily discover that, for one group of scientists, a theory that claims the origin of man not merely from the "apes" but also from "dead matter" undermines their belief in the dignity of man, which is the indispensable basis of all human morality. We should note in turn that, for another group, desirable human behavior is based on the belief that there is a unity in nature that embraces all things.

In truth, many scientists would say that scientific theories "should" be based only on purely scientific grounds. But, exactly speaking, what does the word *should* mean in this context? With all the preceding arguments it can mean only: If we consider exclusively the technological purpose of scientific theories, we could exclude all criterions such as agreement with common sense or fitness for supporting desirable conduct. But even if we have firmly decided to do away with all "nonsense," there still remains the criterion of "simplicity," which is necessary for technological purposes and also contains, as we learned previously, a certain sociological judgment. Here, restriction to the purely technological purpose does not actually lead unambiguously to a scientific theory. The only way to include theory-building in the general science of human behavior is to refrain from ordering around scientists by telling them what they "should" do and to find how each special purpose can be achieved by a theory. Only in this way can science as a human activity be "scientifically" understood and the gap between the scientific and the humanistic aspect be abridged.

A Pragmatic Theory of Induction

by C. West Churchman

THE PURPOSE here is to outline the problem of induction when this problem is phrased in pragmatic terms—that is, when the problem is phrased in terms of the relationship between evidence and decisions. Pragmatism is presumably interested in the relationship of actions to actions and not simply in the relationship of "sentences" to "sentences." Hence, the pragmatic problem of induction must be stated in a language of human actions—that is, in the language of the social sciences.

The following terms appear to be critical: *evidence gathering,* which is a reaction of an individual to the environment, when such reaction is considered from the viewpoint of an increase in knowledge of the individual relative to a set of objectives; *decision,* which is a potential action of an individual, when such action is considered from the viewpoint of its efficiency for accomplishing one or more objectives; *efficiency,* which is the probability (or some analogous measure) that a decision will produce an outcome; *objective,* which is a state of nature, or part of a state of nature, potentially producible by a decision; *value,* which is a measure associated with each objective; *policy* (strategy), which is a rule for the selection of a decision out of a set of decisions at a moment of time; this rule may be such as to determine uniquely the decision, or the rule may specify a random device (flipping a coin) for the selection; *increase in knowledge,* which is a measure of the efficiency of a policy over a period of time relative to a set of objectives and their values.

These definitions are intentionally interdependent (circular), based on the methodological supposition that definitions are not analytic (reductions to simples) but rather interconceptual (exhibitions of the interrelationships of concepts).

The pragmatic problem of induction is the determination of the optimum relationship between evidence gathering and the determination of policies. The problem includes not only the relation of *given* evidence to policy formation but also the relation of the policies of gathering evidence to other types of policies (for example, the sampling theory and experimental design theories are evidence-gathering policies).

The pragmatic problem of induction depends, among other things, on a determination of the efficiency of policies. Some policies are considered "rational," some are not. Can this concept be defined and measured? This paper exhibits the types of problems that arise in connection with a definition of policy efficiency. Problems may be classified into the following types.

1) *Deterministic one-aim problems with certainty,* where (i) decisions are judged in terms of one objective; (ii) there exists a finite set of evidence sufficient to determine the efficiency of a decision for the objective; (iii) every decision has either a perfect chance of success or a zero chance. Examples are puzzles, simple games, and some mathematical derivations. Here it seems clear that there is only one "perfect" policy consisting of the decision to gather the minimum evidence set necessary to guarantee a perfect decision leading to the objective. The effectiveness of other policies may be measured in terms of the additional "surplus" evidence gathering necessary to find the perfect solution.

2) *Statistical one-aim problems with certainty,* where (i) decisions are judged in terms of one objective; (ii) there exists a finite set of evidence (virtually) sufficient to determine the efficiency of a decision for the objective; (iii) every decision has a definite probability of attaining the objective. Simple gambling games are examples. The efficiency of policies can be measured in terms of the "surplus" of evidence gathering plus the efficiency of the decision that is chosen, although the exact form of this measurement may not always be clear.

3) *One-aim problems with double uncertainty,* where (i) one objective is to be served; (ii) each decision has a

definite probability of success relative to the objective; (iii) there exists no finite set of evidence sufficient to determine the possibilities of success of the decisions; (iv) estimates of the probabilities can be made, and estimates of the errors of these estimates can be made. Examples are simple scientific theories, where "curiosity-satisfaction" is the objective, or a company's policy, where so-called net return or profit, is the only objective. Such problems are "doubly uncertain," because the decisions are not certain to produce the desired result, and because the "uncertainty" can only be estimated within error limits.

Here the measures of efficiency of a policy become less easily definable. One might argue for the policy that leads to the maximum *estimated* probability of success. This intuitive guess, however, would in some cases be incorrect, for the errors of the estimates might be quite critical. For example, let us suppose that one decision is estimated to have a probability of success of 0.75 but that the error of this estimate is 0.25. That is to say, the *true* probability may lie anywhere between 0.5 and 1.0. The second decision is estimated to have a probability of success of 0.70, but this estimate is accurate within 0.01. That is, the true value should lie between 0.69 and 0.71. A policy that selects the first decision is not clearly the best policy. It would be the best policy only if one believed that nature "is either beneficent or indifferent." The choice of the second decision may be a far better one, especially if one believes that nature is inclined to be an opponent.

In this case then, the effectiveness of a policy is to be measured by some function of the evidence-gathering effort, the estimated probabilities of the success of the decisions, and the errors of these estimates. The form of this function is not "clear."

4) *Multiaim problems with double uncertainty,* where (i) more than one objective is to be served by the policy; (ii) no decision has maximum effectiveness for all the objectives; (iii) a definite probability of success exists for each decision relative to each objective; (iv) there exists no finite set of evidence sufficient to guarantee the probabilities of success; (v) the probabilities of success can be estimated, and the errors of these estimates can also be estimated; (vi) the values of the objectives are known or assumed without error. Examples are policy problems of agencies, industries,

and so forth, where the goals are accepted as definitive. Here a policy is judged in terms of the evidence-gathering effort, the estimated probabilities of success of the decisions relative to each objective, the errors of these estimates, and the "given" values of the objectives. The proper form of this function becomes even less "clear."

5) *Multiaim problems with triple uncertainty,* where (i) more than one objective is to be served; (ii) no decision has maximum effectiveness for all objectives; (iii) a definite probability of success exists for each decision relative to each objective; (iv) there exists no finite set of evidence sufficient to guarantee the probabilities of success; (v) the probabilities of success can be estimated, and the errors of these estimates can be estimated; (vi) there exists no finite set of evidence sufficient to guarantee the values of the objectives; (vii) the values of the objectives can be estimated, and the errors of these estimates can be estimated. Examples are all scientific, community, and industrial problems. The evaluation of policies in this last problem is the least "clear" of any; the measure of evaluation is *some* function of the estimates of the probabilities of success and the values and the errors of these estimates.

Possible attacks on the pragmatic problem of induction are:

1) Science ends in summarizing its evidence, and it has no part in the evaluation of policies. The objection to this viewpoint is that science obviously makes decisions of its own in both theoretical and applied science. Science must decide to take certain steps in its procedures, and these steps must presumably be evaluated by science. Since science does make decisions, the question is: How does it evaluate its own policies? Or it is unquestionably true that there are not undecided policy decisions of basic science? Are all the issues decided by what the "best" scientists actually do?

2) The evaluation of policies is a concern of science, but it is relative only to "given" values of the objectives and "given" attitudes toward risks. In other words, science does not estimate the values of objectives, since these must be given by "executive" or "popular" judgment. Hence, triple-uncertainty problems are meaningless to science. If this position is adopted, science itself can be evaluated only on relative grounds.

3) Values can be assigned by science to objectives, and the criterions of best decision can also be assigned. To accomplish this assignment and still accept the circularity involved (science must accept values to study values), it is necessary to develop a theory of science in which no scientific conclusion ever has complete validity and in which the methodology used by science is a self-correcting device.

A typical model for this type of science has been developed within statistical quality control, and its application to scientific method is expressed in an article by Sebastian Littauer (1). "Ethical" considerations relative to the values of the objectives also have been discussed (2, 3). The general notion developed in (1) is that science does not come to conclusions, does not validate them, and so forth, but that science is essentially a control device. Specifically, scientific procedures provide policies of such a nature that if a decision is selected wrongly the procedure will indicate the incorrectness of the wrong solution earlier or more economically than any other method. That is to say, a method is scientific insofar as it presents controls at the best possible moment for the individuals involved. The perfect scientific method would thus provide perfect controls at every instant, and approximations to such an ideal are more or less scientific according to the degree of approximation.

This solution operates as follows. One assumes a criterion for the value of policies and uses it as a basis for the solution of the problem of induction. Evidence is then gathered and set into the total system—a system that includes a method whereby one can determine whether the evidence indicates the correctness of the "basic" assumption for evaluating policies. The circularity of the system then becomes a rather vast control mechanism by which the assumptions of the system are checked and their invalidity is determined at the earliest possible moment. A system would be "vicious" if it were such that no set of evidence statements could ever reveal the incorrectness of the assumptions by which the system operates. A system *could* be circular and nonvicious according to this definition. The pious hope or faith of those interested in science is that there exists a nonvicious circular system, that is, a system of scientific gathering of evidence, and evaluation of policies thereby, which continually provides for self-adjustment of this system with a consequent closer approximation to the perfect controlled system.

NOTES

1. S. B. Littauer, *Phil of Sci.* **21**, 93 (1954).
2. C. W. Churchman, *ibid.* **20**, 257 (1933).
3. ———, "Philosophy of experimentation," *Proc. Biostatics Conf.*, Iowa State College, Ames (1952).

Value Judgments in the Acceptance
of Theories

by Richard Rudner

AN IMPORTANT UNDERLYING POINT in the other three articles of this chapter is the manner in which, if at all, value judgments impinge on the process of validating scientific hypotheses and theories.

I think that such validations do *essentially* involve the making of value judgments in a typically ethical issue. And I emphasize *essentially* to indicate my feeling that not only do scientists, as a matter of psychological fact, make value judgments in the course of such validations—since as human beings they are so constituted as to make this virtually unavoidable—but also that the making of such judgments is *logically* involved in the validation of scientific hypotheses; and consequently that a logical reconstruction of this process would entail the statement that a value judgment is a requisite step in the process.

My reasons for believing this may be set forth briefly, but before presenting them I should like to distinguish my thesis as clearly as I can from apparently similar ones that have traditionally been offered.

Traditionally, the involvement of value judgments (in some typically ethical sense) in science has ordinarily been argued on three grounds: (i) Our having a science at all, or, at any rate, our voluntary engagement in such activities, in itself presupposes a value judgment. (ii) To be able to select among alternative problems, or, at any rate, among alternative foci of his interests, the scientist must make a value judgment. (iii) The scientist cannot escape his quite human self. He is a "mass of predilections," and these predilections must inevitably influence all his activities—not excepting his scientific ones. These traditional arguments have never seemed entirely adequate, and the responses that some empirically oriented philosophers and some scientists have made to them have been telling. These responses have generally had the following import.

If it is necessary to make a value decision to have a science before we can have one, then this decision is literally prescientific and has not, therefore, been shown to be any part of the *procedures* of science. Similarly, the decision that one problem is more worth while as a focus of attention than another is an extraproblematic decision and forms no part of the procedures involved in dealing with the problem *decided* upon. Since it is these procedures that constitute the method of science, the value judgment has not thus been shown to be involved in the scientific method as such.

With respect to the presence of our predilections in the laboratory, most empirically oriented philosophers and scientists agree that this is "unfortunately" the case; but, they hasten to add, if science is to progress toward objectivity, the influence of our personal feelings or biases on experimental results must be minimized. We must try not to let our personal idiosyncrasies affect our scientific work. The perfect scientist—the scientist *qua* scientist—does not allow this kind of value judgment to influence his work. However much he may find doing so unavoidable, *qua* father, *qua* lover, *qua* member of society, *qua* grouch, *when* he does so he is not behaving *qua* scientist. Consequently, a logical reconstruction of the scientific method would not need, on this account, to include a reference to the making of value judgments. From such considerations it would seem that the traditional arguments for the involvement of value judgments in science lack decisiveness.

But I think a different and somewhat stronger argument can be made. I assume that no analysis of what constitutes the method of science would be satisfactory unless it comprised some assertion to the effect that the scientist validates—that is, accepts or rejects—hypotheses. But if this is so, then clearly the scientist does make value judgments. Since no scientific hypothesis is ever completely verified, n accepting a hypothesis on the basis of evidence, the scientist must make the decision that the evidence is *sufficiently* strong or that the probability is *sufficiently* high to warrant the acceptance of the hypothesis. Obviously, our decision with regard to the evidence and how strong is "strong enough" is going to be a function of the *importance*, in the typically ethical sense, of making a mistake in accepting or rejecting the hypothesis. Thus, to take a crude but easily manageable example, if the hypothesis under consideration stated that a toxic ingredient of a drug was not present in lethal quantity, then we would require a relatively high degree of confirmation or confidence before accepting the hypothesis—for the consequences of making a mistake here are exceedingly grave by our moral standards. In contrast, if our hypothesis stated that, on the basis of some sample, a certain lot of machine-stamped belt buckles was not defective, the degree of confidence we would require would be relatively lower. *How sure we must be before we accept a hypothesis depends on how serious a mistake would be.*

The examples I have chosen are from scientific inferences in industrial quality control. But the point is clearly quite general in application. It would be interesting and instructive, for example, to know how high a degree of probability the Manhattan Project scientists demanded for the hypothesis that no uncontrollable pervasive chain reaction would occur before they proceeded with the first atomic bomb detonation or even first activated the Chicago pile above a critical level. It would be equally interesting and instructive to know how they decided that the chosen probability value (if one was chosen) was high enough rather than one that was higher; on the other hand, it is conceivable that the problem, in this form, was not brought to consciousness at all.

In general, then, before we can accept any hypothesis, the value decision must be made in the light of the seriousness of a mistake, and the degree of probability must be *high enough* or the evidence must be *strong enough* to warrant its acceptance.

Some empiricists, confronted with the foregoing considerations, agree that *acceptance* or *rejection* of hypotheses essentially involves value judgments, but they are nonetheless loath to accept the conclusion; instead they have denied the premise that it is the business of the scientist *qua* scientist to validate hypotheses or theories. They have argued that the scientist's task is *only to determine the strength of the evidence* for a hypothesis and not, as scientist, to accept or reject the hypothesis.

But a little reflection shows that the plausibility of this as an objection is merely apparent. The determination that the degree of confirmation is, say, *p* or that the strength of the evidence is such and such, which is on this view the indispensable task of the scientist *qua* scientist, is clearly nothing more than *the acceptance, by the scientist, of the hypothesis that the degree of confidence is p or that the strength of the evidence is such and such;* and, as these men have conceded, acceptance of hypotheses does require value decisions.

If the major point I have tried to establish is correct, then we are confronted with a first-order crisis in science and methodology. The positive horror with which most scientists and philosophers of science view the intrusion of value considerations into science is wholly understandable. Memories of the conflict, now abated but to a certain extent still continuing, between science and, for example, the dominant religions over the intrusion of religious value considerations into the domain of scientific inquiry are strong in many reflective scientists. The traditional search for objectivity exemplifies science's pursuit of one of its most precious ideals. For the scientist to close his eyes to the fact that scientific method *intrinsically* requires the making of value decisions, and for him to push out of his consciousness the fact that he does make them, can in no way bring him closer to the ideal of objectivity. To refuse to pay attention to the value decisions that *must* be made, to make them intuitively, unconsciously, and haphazardly, is to leave an essential aspect of scientific method scientifically out of control.

What seems necessary (and no more than the sketchiest indications of the problem can be given here) is nothing less than a radical reworking of the ideal of scientific objectivity. The naive conception of the scientist as one who is cold-blooded, emotionless, impersonal, and passive, mirroring the world perfectly in the highly polished lenses of his steel-rimmed glasses is no longer, if it ever was, adequate.

What is proposed here is that objectivity for science lies

t least in becoming precise about what value judgments
re being made and might have been made in a given in-
uiry—and, stated in the most challenging form, what value
ecisions ought to be made.

nfluence of Political Creeds on the

cceptance of Theories

by Barrington Moore, Jr.

ᶠEW PEOPLE TODAY are likely to argue that the acceptance
ᵒf scientific theories, even by scientists themselves, depends
ntirely upon the logical evidence adduced in support of
hese theories. Extraneous factors related to the philosophi-
al climate and society in which the scientist lives always
ᵖlay at least some part. The interesting problem, therefore,
ᵉcomes not one of ascertaining the existence of such factors
ᵘut one of appraising the extent of their impact under dif-
erent conditions. My task here (1) is confined to interpret-
ng a few high lights of the evidence I have been able to
ᵍather on this point for the Soviet Union. A much fuller
ᵈiscussion is available in a recently published general study
ᵒf the sources of stability and change in the Soviet dictator-
hip (2).

Since others in this symposium discuss the content of the
ᵒfficial orthodoxy, dialectical materialism, there is no need
ᵒr me to deal with this topic in any detail. I should like,
ᵒwever, to draw attention to two features. One is that the
ᵈoctrine has a strong bias against formal and abstract think-
ng, such as that found in pure mathematics, symbolic
ᵒgic, and much of modern physics. The other is this: We
ᵃll know that the doctrine pretends to be a universal and
ᵒsmic explanation of all natural and human phenomena.
Yet, as a practical matter, the areas where it is applied and
he ways in which it is interpreted vary considerably with
ᵔhanging political circumstances. There is, therefore, a
ᵈuctuating and ill-defined boundary, a sort of no man's land,
ᵇetween the area of politically determined truth and the
area of scientifically determined truth. From about the end

of World War II until Stalin's death, the area of political truth expanded steadily, not only in genetics, but also in physics, chemistry, and mathematics. Since Stalin's death there have been numerous signs of a retreat on the intellectual front. There have not, however, been any significant changes in the control machinery itself.

There are two main ways in which the Soviet system attempts to bring about the political orthodoxy of science. One way is through giving the more distinguished scientists higher incomes and greater material comforts than the rest of the population. This high social and economic status is held upon the condition of outward political conformity. The other method is administrative. Soviet science is highly bureaucratized. The independent scientist working on his own and freely choosing his own problems does not exist in the U.S.S.R. Instead, he must find his niche in a rambling bureaucratic structure. This state of affairs is, of course, by no means wholly attributable to the totalitarian aspects of the Soviet system. Probably it is a product of change brought about by the development of industrial society generally. Indeed, the easiest way for an American to capture the atmosphere of Soviet science would be to recall our large government research projects, although there are significant distinctions between the two situations.

It is unnecessary to present here a detailed analysis of the administrative apparatus in Soviet science. Essentially, it is composed of three elements, the Communist Party, the secret police, and the technically qualified scientist, a triumvirate that has its counterpart in every Soviet organization from a scientific laboratory to a factory, an army unit, a sports club, or a collective farm. A few comments on the ways in which this control system does and does not affect actual scientific work may be of interest.

The aspect of Soviet science that is perhaps most puzzling to us in the Western world is the notion of planning. In actual practice, the plan or research program of any given laboratory often represents the outcome of a tug of war between the desires of the political leaders and the wishes of the scientists themselves. Despite numerous efforts to tighten controls after the war, there are clear indications that the natural scientists managed to retain a good deal of autonomy, or at least much more autonomy than the rulers would like. For example, in October 1952, a high Party official from Leningrad, Moscow's rival as the chief center of scientific activity in the U.S.S.R., observed sarcastically in a public speech that the hand of the State Planning Commission could not be felt in his city's scientific research establishments.

In general, it appears that the forms of direct control, such as planning and probably even the continuous barrage of Marxist-Leninist propaganda, have less effect on the content of Soviet science and, hence, on what the Soviet scientist accepts as valid theory than do somewhat more subtle factors. In this connection, I hasten to add that I am not a natural scientist myself and that it would require someone with both sociological skills and the appropriate natural science skills to confirm or disprove this tentative judgment. But one may point to certain factors connected with the career expectation of Soviet scientists as major elements in influencing the choice that they make among various bodies of thought. The most effective power of the Communist regime lies, I think, in deciding which kinds of research will be rewarded upon completion and which kinds of research will in effect be penalized. The immediate point of impact is on the career expectations of advanced students as well as on mature scientists who want to progress up the ladder of rank and prestige. Since some calculation of these factors must be made on a "realistic" basis by even the most idealistic or the most strictly logical scientist, the force of these controls extends backward to an early stage in the scientist's career. It is especially important at the time the scientist selects his field of study. However, it is only when a student reaches the closing period of his university studies that he knows whether or not he has placed his chips wisely.

The major elements in the situation are the following. The Ministry of Culture is responsible for confirming appointments to research and teaching staffs and for granting higher degrees, although the initial recommendations are usually made by qualified scientists and scholars. In 1951, the Ministry refused to grant 10.7 per cent of the doctoral degrees that had been recommended during the preceding three years. No indication is available as to how many of these refusals were based on strictly political grounds. But the reports of the Ministry, which receive wide publicity in the central newspapers, usually select several cases of refusal on political grounds to serve as warnings to Soviet youth. Thus, in 1948, the authorities refused to confer the title of professor upon a doctor of physicomathematical sciences, V. L. Ginzburg, on the grounds that he had, even in his popular works, circumvented the achievements of Soviet science and displayed obvious servility toward foreign achievements.

There is also evidence that students, in calculating their chances for a career, tend to choose either a subject in which the Party has laid down a clear and definite line or one about which the Party has expressed no opinion. In other words, they choose either the areas where political truths are definite or where scientific truths can be more or less freely ascertained. They try to steer clear of dangerous border areas. Thus, students avoided writing dissertations on genetics for quite some time before the Party made Lysenko's views an official orthodoxy, a decision that was not reached until a series of minor forays had been made by the Party into this area. Three years before the Lysenko decision, a high Soviet official complained that dissertations on genetics were becoming so rare as to be almost unique events. But in history and philosophy, on which the Party made a series of clear-cut pronouncements after the war, there was a sixfold rise in the number of dissertations, while the total increase in all fields during this period amounted to only 34.4 per cent.

Since the Soviets place a very high value on certain kinds of scientific research and technical training, the Party and the police do not ordinarily interfere in the routine activities of the scientist. In fields where the Party has not issued a pronouncement, the scientist can set his own standards for governing the appraisal of evidence and reasoning in research and can set corresponding standards for the qualifications of his students. By the late 1930's, it became possible for a teacher to fail a Komsomol, or Party member, who was clearly incompetent, although the teacher might have an anxious moment in the process. It appears that this situation prevails widely in many areas of research in the natural sciences at any given moment. The propagation of Marxism-Leninism tends to be reduced to a formality, accepted as a boring necessity by all concerned. In this fashion, the rulers reach a compromise with the autonomous and distinctive requirements of scientific activity.

In the latter years of Stalin's regime, however, this compromise was at least partly upset in several fields. The discussion of genetics in the summer of 1948 is the incident that has attracted the most attention in the West. This event was merely part of a much larger movement. Philosophy, biology, linguistics, physiology, cosmogony, chemistry, physics, and mathematics have all, in widely varying degrees, felt the impact of this movement. In June 1951, to cite merely one example, the Academy of Sciences itself was forced to put the stamp of disapproval on the use of quantum theory, mainly because of its supposed connection with "decadent" Western idealism and formalist abstraction. Although Soviet scientists undoubtedly continue to use quantum theory in their actual work, uncertainty about where the political lightning may strike next must be a vital element in the over-all situation confronting them. The partial relaxation that has followed Stalin's death can scarcely have removed this anxiety. Soviet scientists with any memory of the past are aware that previous periods of relaxation have been followed by new and stricter orthodoxies, and they will remain on their guard.

The examination of the Soviet case prompts some general reflections on the influence of political creeds in science. A totalitarian creed that claims to encompass all human affairs in one sweep is bound to come into conflict with scientific theory at some point. The essence of a totalitarian system is that it tries to impose some single criterion of appropriate behavior on every aspect of human action, from the choice of a marriage partner to the choice of scientific beliefs. Naturally it does not succeed entirely, and it has to come to terms with the autonomous requirements of these activities. As long as a totalitarian regime seeks the benefits of science, it must make some compromise with the scientists' own methods of reaching and determining truth. The compromise may be made easier where the rationalist ethic, that which is part and parcel of the rise of our industrial civilization, has destroyed any sense of moral and ethical commitment among scientists. Then scientists may be quite willing to accept political direction from any source.

A democratic creed, on the other hand, does not claim to present answers to all possible questions or to pose the way in which all human activities must be carried out. The way it attempts to solve the problem of reaching some kind of harmony in all the affairs of society, including scientific

affairs, is a different one and provides greater flexibility
Up to a point, the democratic creed provides for its own
modification through established and agreed-upon rules
Such modifications can come from science as well as from
other sources.

I would suggest, however, that no society, not even a
democratic one, can accept science as the sole method and
source for the modification of its established creed. For rea
sons that cannot be given here in any detail, it appear
likely that any large human society requires a set of belief
about the purposes of life and the ways in which it is le
gitimate and not legitimate to achieve these purposes. Thi
set of beliefs constitutes the political truths of the society
Since they involve judgments of value, I do not think tha
they can ever be completely amenable to rational discussion
Therefore, as science develops its own canons for validating
its propositions, there is likely to come a time when the
political creed and the scientific creed conflict with each
other. I am inclined to believe that some element of con
flict will usually be present, despite the contemporary ef
forts of some religious and scientific authorities to make
polite bows in each other's direction. Methods of contro
and compromise will then have to be found. At any rate
the conflict is a familiar one in the history of Western culture

In other words, the totalitarian case, including that o
the U.S.S.R., merely constitutes an extreme one. The situa
tion there does not differ from our own in any absolute
sense. Nor can all the features of the Soviet scene that many
of us find repugnant be traced entirely to the totalitarian
bacillus. In the growth of organized research, the emphasi
on practical results, and the stress on political conformity
one can perceive in the Soviet situation elements that rep
resent, as it were, a horrible image in a distorted mirror o
our own possible future. Major similarities can be traced
to the fact that both the United States and the Soviet Union
are industrial societies.

Fortunately, the situation in Russia is only a possible
image of our future and is by no means an inevitable one
As E. H. Carr has remarked, history does not repeat itself
because the actors on the stage already know the outcome
of the previous act (3). The experience of others, to the
extent that we understand it and use it, becomes part of ou
own situation and helps us to make it different. Let us hope

that fuller understanding of Soviet science may help the West to avoid a similar fate.

NOTES

1. I wish to acknowledge my debt to the Russian Research Center of Harvard University, under whose auspices this work was done.
2. B. Moore, Jr., *Terror and Progress—U.S.S.R.* (Harvard Univ. Press, Cambridge, Mass., 1954).
3. *The New Society* (London, 1951), p. 6.

The Present State of Operations

Chapter 2

The Present State of Operationalism

Interpretations and Misinterpretations

of Operationalism

by Henry Margenau

IN INTRODUCING THIS SYMPOSIUM on "The present state of operationalism," I deem it proper to keep my remarks brief and general, leaving criticism and appraisal to the active participants.

Operationalism is an attitude that emphasizes the need of recourse, wherever feasible, to instrumental procedures when meanings are to be established. Bridgman disavows its status as a philosophy, and wisely so, for as a general view it would be vulnerable on two counts. First, it cannot define the meaning of "instrumental procedure" in a manner that saves the view from being either trivial (which would be true if "instrumental" were construed to include symbolic, mental and paper-and-pencil operations) or too restrictive (if all operations are to be laboratory procedures). Second, it fails to impart meaning to substantive concepts—that is, concepts related to entities that are regarded as the carriers of operationally determinable qualities or quantities. To illustrate this latter point: it is possible to define, in terms of instrumental procedures, the charge, the mass, and the spin of an electron, but hardly the electron itself.

Yet every scientist feels the value of the operational approach. I shall try to indicate the reason for this by showing that operational definitions occupy a critical role in the methodology of science.

If, as is customary in much of traditional philosophy, we recognize within our cognitive experience two dominating poles, the *rational* (concepts, constructs, ideas, and so on) and the *immediate* (such as sensations, observations, and data), then there arises the problem of bridging the two. For it is clear that a concept is not identical with, or inductively derivable from, a set of percepts. The nonempirical requirements that render fertile and consistent the constructs of a given theory (in *The Nature of Physical Reality*, McGraw-Hill, 1950, I have called them "metaphysical requirements") can be stated without reference to actual observations; hence, they do not validate or reify the constructs they confine but establish them merely as an internally consistent set, a formal theory. The empirical requirement, the possibility of circuits of factual verification that mediate between observational data and constructs, confers validity, and such circuits are impossible without operational definitions—operational in terms of performed or imagined *laboratory procedures*.

This implies that operations are not the only means of defining scientific concepts; indeed, the analysis shows precisely why they alone are insufficient. A valid concept must belong to a satisfactory theory which obeys the metaphysical rules. This it cannot do unless it is susceptible to a formal definition that links it nonoperationally to other concepts or terms of the theory. But it must also be empirically verifiable, and this requires a linkage with observations via operational procedures. Thus, it is necessary, and a survey of scientific method shows this to be true, that every accepted scientific measurable quantity have at least two definitions, one formal and one instrumental. It is an interesting task to show how some sciences fail to become exact because they ignore this dual character of the definitory process. Omission of operational definitions leads to sterile speculation, to metaphysics in the sense of the detractors of that discipline; disregard of formal (or "constitutive") definitions leads to that blind empiricism which misses the power and the beauty of modern physical science.

Sense and Nonsense in Operationism

by Gustav Bergmann

A PHILOSOPHY or philosophic position is a system of mutually consistent and interdependent explications of and answers to philosophic questions with the implicit claim that all such questions—those that have been asked in the past as well as those that may be asked in the future—can be clarified in the style or manner of the system. The number of points actually dealt with must, therefore, be large enough to provide an adequate idea of the style or manner. By this token, operationism is not a philosophic position. Its concern is with one point and one point only. More conservatively still, operationism, in any sense both reasonable and reasonably specific, is merely a footnote, though an important one, to a point that has received much attention and has been accepted by many philosophers, at least since Locke first distinguished between simple and complex ideas. I shall first state the point, then the footnote.

Imagine one who knows the grammar of our language and understands its logical words but understands only a part of its descriptive vocabulary. Call this part his *basic descriptive vocabulary*. If this basis is properly chosen, such a one can, in principle, be taught to understand any descriptive term by presenting him, within our language, with its definition. This is the point. In stating it I managed to avoid, at least verbally, the controversial notion of meaning. I did this because I believe that some of the nonsense that is now being said about meaning is not unconnected with some vague notion of operationism. To this sort of thing I shall briefly attend in my last comment. But the notion of definition, which I could not avoid, is also controversial, not perhaps like meaning in first philosophy, yet precisely in the context in which I used it. I add, then, that I use it at the moment in a sense broad enough to preclude controversy. This broad sense includes definitions properly speaking, that is, definitions whose definienda are eliminable; it includes partial definitions (whatever it may mean for a definition to be partial), that is, so-called reduction pairs; it even includes what more commonly, and I think less confusingly, is called the interpretation of axiomatic calculi. In this broad sense of definition, the point is, to repeat, the definability of our descriptive vocabulary in terms of a part of it.

The footnote is a comment on the logic of concept formation in science. This limitation of range has two consequences. For one, the terms whose definability or definitions are asserted or examined are merely the concepts of the several sciences, particularly, as one says, very loosely but quite intelligibly, the more abstract ones. For another, the basic vocabulary may be assumed to contain only the simplest terms of what Carnap once called the thing language.

Informally speaking, it does not exceed that of an unsophisticated laboratory attendant. Consider now, without prejudice, the case of an explicit definition, say, that of a very primitive notion of length. The definition being of the kind called in use, the definiendum is not the single term 'length' (*1*) but a whole sentence, say, in an instance, 'The length of this ledge is three feet.' The definiens proposed is a conditional, 'If *A* then *B*'; where '*A*' is a statement of the measuring procedure, namely, the laying off in a certain manner of a foot rule, and '*B*' a statement of what one observes after one has performed this operation, namely, the coincidence of one corner of the ledge with one end of the foot rule at the third step. Generally one may say, again without prejudice as to detail, that the definiens states what one must do and what, having done it, one must see in order to assert the truth of the simplest kind of statement in which the new term occurs. This comment, with its emphasis on what we do and that we often must do something, manipulatively, if we want to find out whether a certain statement is true, is the important footnote operationalism has contributed.

All this is completely noncontroversial. Equally noncontroversial is, to my mind, the proper answer to an objector who voices, as it were, certain apprehensions of commonsense realism. "What you say," so the objection goes, "sounds suspiciously as if you thought you were somehow making the ledge's length when you measured it. Yet, the ledge has a length that is there and, in particular, the length of three feet whether or not you or anybody else measures it." Here is what I would answer. "The query for what there is, the so-called ontological question, belongs to first philosophy. It cannot even be discussed intelligently in this narrow context, and the logic of scientific concept formation, with or without the operationist footnote, has no bearing on it whatsoever. If it will help to convince you that this is so, I am prepared, as long as we talk in this very general fashion, to put the conditional in the subjunctive, 'If one *were* to do this and this, then one *would* observe that and that.' On the other hand, if you want to *know* how long the ledge is and have no means of inferring it from something else that you already know, then you will indeed have to measure it. This is perfectly common-sensical. So you need not fear that by admitting it you have fallen into a philosophic trap."

Fundamentally, this is all that needs to be said about operationism as such. If, however, one is to survey sense and nonsense around it, one should, perhaps, do three more things. First, one may take stock of the more technical disagreements, on which both sides make sense. Second, one may explore, as an analytic historian of recent ideas, the impact of the doctrine on the several sciences. Third, one should at least identify some of the philosophic nonsense that was either stimulated by or is in some fashion congenial to an exuberant notion of operationism. I shall briefly take up these three topics in this order.

The finer technical points all hinge on how broad a notion of definition the thesis requires. In taking stock of them, as I said I would, rather than discussing them once more in detail, my main purpose is to trace the disagreements in this limited area to the several positions taken on certain philosophic issues, issues that are much more pervasive and fundamental.

Some concepts are introduced not by definitions in the narrower sense, either complete or incomplete, but by the interpretation of axiomatic calculi. On this, as far as I know, everybody who is at all interested in these questions agrees. Everybody agrees, for instance, though perhaps not for the same reasons, that the terms of quantum mechanics must be so introduced. There is disagreement, and that not very serious, only on how much can be achieved without resorting to this procedure. The salient feature of the latter is the freedom it affords to introduce terms that have by themselves no empirical counterparts, that is, counterparts presumably introduced by chains of definitions in the narrower sense. Let me sacrifice pointless generality to the advantages of an illustration and consider the kinetic theory of gases of, say, 1890. The empirical terms are in this case those of phenomenological thermodynamics; the calculus is the so-called mechanical model. Such terms and phrases as 'molecule,' 'the position of a molecule,' and 'the momentum of a molecule' have by themselves no corresponding empirical terms. This peculiarity is now sometimes being talked about in a manner I find confusing. Specifically, I would not say, as some who say certain things now would have had to say consistently had they lived in 1890, that it was then "operationally meaningless" to attribute position or momentum to an individual molecule. Saying any such thing implies a censure that is completely unjustified, irrespective of the eventual success or failure of the theory. Or, to use for once that dangerous word, what is here involved is merely a question of economy, not the much more radical one of meaning. The lack of economy one may charge, which is now sometimes spoken of as the excess meaning of a model, has, of course, its advantages as well as its price.

Concerning the question how soon, as it were, one is reduced to the interpretation of axiomatic calculi, I wish to comment on a recent statement by Hempel (2). Examining in detail how real numbers enter into scientific statements, he first reminds us, with his usual lucidity, of the gap that separates real numbers from the crude fractions we can manipulatively represent and then argues that the accurate bridging of this gap requires the interpretation of axiomatic calculi. I have, of course, no quarrel with the argument. I merely deplore the emphasis. I deplore it because I believe that if in any given case the use of real numbers were the only reason why definitions in the narrower sense break down, it would still be worth while to investigate how far we could get by definitions alone if we forewent the convenience of real numbers. In other words, one should try to bring out the differences between, say, length and a ψ-function, rather than put them in the same boat, for a reason that is fairly obvious. For the real numbers are merely a part of the logical apparatus; concept formation is a matter of the descriptive vocabulary. So it will be well to put to one side the specific problems of the former in order to get an unencumbered view of the latter. To say the same thing differently, one may start with the interpretation of an axiomatic calculus, so that real numbers can be used once and for all, and then ask how much can be done in this calculus by means of definitions alone. But then, all this goes to show that my demurrer is merely a matter of perspective. It is not in itself a disagreement on either fact or logic.

Those who disagree on the respective scope and merit of explicit definition and reduction pairs also share common ground. In fact, it is on this ground that the issue must eventually be joined. Both sides believe that for a technical discussion it is necessary to construct formalisms or ideal

anguages that are, in a familiar sense, abstracts or schematic
reconstructions of our natural language. For the rest, there
are two issues in this area, not one. An explicit definition is
also complete in that, if it is once stated, nothing can be
added to it; to add to it or to change it otherwise is to pro-
pose an alternative reconstruction. Reduction pairs may be
supplemented by further reduction pairs. The one issue is
thus completeness versus incompleteness in this sense. The
other is eliminability versus noneliminability, for the definienda of explicit definitions are eliminable. Reduction pairs
lack this feature and are, therefore, not literally definitions
in the traditional logical sense. I turn first to the second
of these issues.

The facts in the case, if I may so call them, are as noncontroversial as the so-called paradoxes of material implication from which they ultimately flow. In those formalisms
that the two sides are willing to accept, it is impossible to
reconstruct with idiomatic accuracy the subjunctive, 'if one
were to do this, one *would* see that,' which I just proffered
in my imaginary exchange to the suspicious realist. Technically this entails that if explicit definitions are used in the
reconstruction, certain statements become in certain cases
false when their idiomatic counterparts are true, and conversely; when reduction pairs are used, their truth values
remain in these cases conveniently indeterminate. The advocates of explicit definition maintain that these disturbing
cases are really quite trivial and that therefore, if their
mechanism is once understood, one need not worry about
them. The philosophic motives behind this stand, which as
I said by far transcend the immediate issue, are two. For
one, these students feel that a so-called definition which
abandons eliminability is not a satisfactory analysis of the
term it introduces. For another, they are convinced that the
formal schema cannot and need not in all details and trait
by trait agree with the idiom. For if it did, how could it serve
its one and only purpose, to be a tool of philosophic analysis
and not, phantastically, an artificial language to be actually
spoken? So the advocates of explicit definition, of which I
am one (3), avail themselves at this point of the leeway that
conviction gives them.

Some see a virtue in the incompleteness of reduction
pairs. They reason as follows. As, say, electrodynamics developed, more and more ways of measuring current were

discovered. Each of these may be thought to provide a new reduction pair. As more and more of these pairs accrue to what remains in a sense the same "definition," the concept defined becomes richer and richer in meaning. This, by the way, is a harmless meaning of 'meaning,' a less slippery synonym being 'significance.' Those who argue this way reject explicit definitions because of their completeness. Supposedly they are too static and cannot do justice to the growing edge of knowledge. The counterargument moves on two levels. First and in principle, the logical analysis of knowledge is not concerned with its growth. To explain this growth is the task of the behavior sciences. To confuse the latter with logical analysis is to adopt the instrumentalist or some other variant of the idealistic position. Second and in detail, the significance of a concept at any given stage of knowledge reflects itself, not in its definition, but in the laws in which it occurs.

Recently incomplete definitions have found a new advocate in Pap (4). According to Pap, the real trouble with complete ones is that they do not allow for the assignment of the proper probabilities, of the kind now called 'probability$_1$,' to scientific theories. That may well be so. I make no claim to expertness on the details of probability$_1$. Only, one who thinks, as I do (5), that probability$_1$ is a blind alley, will naturally not be impressed by the new twist. This, however, is a different story and, again, one far more important than what is directly at stake between the critics and the defenders of reduction pairs.

Operationism, both the idea and the word, originated within physics. Its manifesto, Bridgman's *The Logic of Modern Physics,* was written by a physicist. The immediate stimulus apparently was Einstein's celebrated analysis of nonlocal simultaneity; understandably enough, since the best way of characterizing his achievement in a very general manner is to say that, having recognized the need for an operational definition of the concept, he proposed one that proved spectacularly significant. Yet, with the Einsteinian revolution consummated, the physical sciences did not stand in great need of the operationist discipline. Accordingly the impact was limited. Occasionally one finds in physicists' writings statements of the kind I criticized when I used the kinetic theory of 1890 as an illustration. I do not think that this kind of mild nonsense or an occasional entirely nonspecific use of the word 'operationism' does much harm in the physical sciences. They are much too set for that.

The impact on psychology was tremendous. Again this is easily understood. Applied to psychological concepts, operationism becomes methodological behaviorism, that is, a behaviorism sobered and shorn of its metaphysics. Operationism can thus take credit for having facilitated the transition from Watsonianism to contemporary behavior theory. To be sure, there was also some nonsense, mostly misunderstandings owing to the philosophic naivety of some psychologists. By now these misunderstandings have happily disappeared; at least, they have been pointed out. The root of the trouble was that some psychologists in their enthusiasm mistook the operationist footnote for the whole philosophy of science, if not for the whole of philosophy. So they thought, first, that operationism also provided rules for assuring the significance of concepts properly defined. There are, of course, no such rules. Second, while operations in the relevant sense are manipulations and nothing else, they saw operations everywhere. At the one extreme, the scientist's perceptions were decked out to be a species of operations; at the other, his verbal and computational activities were as so-called symbolic operations herded into the same corral. This completely nonspecific use of 'operation' proved confusing. And there was still another confusion. To give an extreme illustration, some refused, presumably on operationist principles, to "generalize" from one instance of an experiment to the next if the apparatus had in the meantime been moved to another corner of the room. Yet, there is no *a priori* rule to distinguish relevant from irrelevant variables. Nor is there any such thing as an exhaustive description. Generally, the operationist fashion provided some specious arguments to those who disliked all sorts of theorizing or, even, conceptualizing. But perhaps it was wholesome that psychology went through this phase.

If physics did not particularly need the operationist discipline and if psychology has accepted it, the case of the group sciences such as economics and sociology is again different. Their outstanding feature is the occurrence of group concepts. The one kind, call it 'statistical,' is exemplified by, say 'average income' and 'export import ratio.' These can obviously be defined statistically in terms of psychological and environmental concepts. Such definability, whether statistical or otherwise, is at the moment not so obvious for the second kind. This kind, call it 'institutional,' is exemplified by, say, 'the Church' and 'the moral code of the Army.' Yet I believe, as probably most philosophers in the empiricist tradition do, that there are only two alternatives. Either institutional concepts are so vague that one may as well give up hope of ever incorporating them into a worth-while science; or they, too, will eventually be defined, or, if you please, operationally defined in terms of psychological and environmental concepts. If I am not mistaken, the group sciences are only now, and not without some resistance, absorbing this idea (6). So the discipline of operationist thinking may still do them some good.

The philosophic nonsense somehow connected with some vague notion of operationism is of two main varieties: the one, an instrumentalist misinterpretation; the other, the so-called operational theory of meaning. The latter, too, has instrumentalist affinities.

Instrumentalism stems from an exaggerated and subtly twisted emphasis on doing or manipulating. Practically, experimentation is indispensable in science, just as we must act if we want to survive. In principle, however, and I put it strongly in order to make the point, if only we lived long enough and were patient enough, we could choose to remain spectators and wait until those situations that we in fact so ingeniously contrive occur, as one says, by chance. Logically, what matters is that they happen, not that we make them happen. This alone shows that the operationist footnote has no tendency whatsoever to give aid and comfort to the strange pseudoscientific subjectivism which wants us to believe that we somehow by our thoughts and actions make or determine what is in itself an indeterminate situation. I, for one, find myself in a world that is quite determinate, not at all of my making and, alas, quite often not to my liking.

Bridgman's well-known formula, "In general, we mean by any concept nothing more than a set of operations; the concept is synonymous with the corresponding set of operations," is perhaps merely a scientist's version of a so-called meaning criterion. So interpreted, it excludes from science terms not defined from a thing-language basic vocabulary.

, as the words would indicate, it excludes the terms of interpreted axiomatic calculi, then it is unduly restrictive. If
is to include them, then the notion of an operation must,
s I just observed, be stretched beyond all reason. But Bridg-
nan's formula could also be a scientist's version of Witt-
enstein's dictum that the meaning of a proposition is the
nethod of its verification. So interpreted, it becomes a
:atement of the verification theory of meaning. A so-called
neory of meaning, by the way, is not the same thing as a
riterion of meaning. A criterion says which terms have
neaning; a theory says what meaning is. Perhaps a verifica-
on theory was what Bridgman had in mind. I do not know.
[is formula lends itself to still another interpretation. Taken
terally, it identifies the meaning of a concept not with its
-ferent, but with the operations one must perform if one
ants to test the presence of this referent. So interpreted,
is an instrumentalist variant of the standard reference
neory. Unfortunately this third reading has been the most
fluential. It is without doubt one of the major sources of
ll the nonsensical talk that passes for an operational theory
f meaning. What seemed attractive in it was probably the
ibstitution of something comfortably concrete, operations,
or something suspiciously abstract, meaning.

Let me say one word in conclusion. Even if one discounts
ome meanings that are not difficult to analyze, 'meaning'
still not a univocal term. Thus no univocal or one-track
neory will do. Philosophers who adopt one must blunder
omewhere sooner or later. But this is not to say that all
nivocal theories are, like the operational one, in them-
-lves clouds of confusion. They may, and I think some of
nem do, explicate important meanings of meaning. This,
owever, is another story (7).

NOTES

In this article, single quotation marks are used to enclose a word
or expression that is mentioned, not used. Double quotation
marks indicate either emphasis or direct quotation.

C. G. Hempel, *Foundations of Concept Formation in Empirical
Science* (Univ. of Chicago Press, Chicago, 1952).

G. Bergmann, "Comments on Professor Hempel's 'The Concept
of cognitive significance,'" *Proc. Am. Acad. Arts Sci.* **80**, 78
(1951); "Comments on Storer's definition of 'soluble,'" *Analysis* **12**, 44 (1951).

4. A. Pap, "Reduction sentences and open concepts," *Methodos* **5** 3 (1953).
5. G. Bergmann, "Some comments on Carnap's logic of induction," *Phil. Sci.* **13**, 71 (1946).
6. A contribution of this kind is made in H. D. Lasswell and A. Kaplan, *Power and Society* (Yale Univ. Press, New Haven, Conn. 1950). See also my review of this book in *Ethics* **52**, 64 (1951). For a systematic discussion of these issues, including so-called reduction, see M. Brodbeck, "On the philosophy of the social sciences," *Phil. Sci.* **21**, 140 (1954).
7. "Logical positivism, language, and the reconstruction of metaphysics," *Riv. Critica di Storia della Filosofia* **8**, 453 (1953) [reprinted in my book, *The Metaphysics of Logical Positivism* (Longmans, Green, New York, 1954)].

A Logical Appraisal of Operationism

by Carl G. Hempel

OPERATIONISM, in its fundamental tenets, is closely akin to logical empiricism. Both schools of thought have put much emphasis on definite experiential meaning or import as necessary condition of objectively significant discourse, and both have made strong efforts to establish explicit criterion of experiential significance. But logical empiricism has treated experiential import as a characteristic of statements—namely, as their susceptibility to test by experiment or observation—whereas operationism has tended to construe experiential meaning as a characteristic of concepts or of the terms representing them—namely, as their susceptibility to operational definition.

Basic ideas of operational analysis. An operational definition of a term is conceived as a rule to the effect that the term is to apply to a particular case if the performance of specified operations in that case yields a certain characteristic result. For example, the term 'harder than' might be operationally defined by the rule that a piece of mineral, x, is to be called harder than another piece of mineral, y, if the operation of drawing a sharp point of x across the surface of y results in a scratch mark on the latter. Similarly, the different numerical values of a quantity such as length are thought of as operationally definable by reference to the outcomes of specified measuring operations. To safeguard the objectivity of science, all operations invoked in this kind of definition are required to be intersubjective in the sense that different observers must be able to perform "the same operation" with reasonable agreement in their results (1).

P. W. Bridgman, the originator of operational analysis, distinguishes several kinds of operation that may be invoked in specifying the meanings of scientific terms (2). The principal ones are (i) what he calls *instrumental operations*—these consist in the use of various devices of observation and measurement—and (ii) paper-and-pencil operations, verbal operations, mental experiments, and the like—this group is meant to include, among other things, the techniques of mathematical and logical inference as well as the use of experiments in imagination. For brevity, but also by way of suggesting a fundamental similarity among the procedures of the second kind, I shall refer to them as *symbolic operations*.

The concepts of operation and of operational definition serve to state the basic principles of operational analysis, of which the following are of special importance.

1) "Meanings are operational." To understand the meaning of a term, we must know the operational criterions of its application (3), and every meaningful scientific term must therefore permit of an operational definition. Such definition may refer to certain symbolic operations and it always must ultimately make reference to some instrumental operation (4).

2) To avoid ambiguity, every scientific term should be defined by means of one unique operational criterion. Even when two different operational procedures (for instance, the optical and the tactual ways of measuring length) have been found to yield the same results, they still must be considered as defining different concepts (for example, optical and tactual length), and these should be distinguished terminologically because the presumed coincidence of the results is inferred from experimental evidence, and it is "not safe" to forget that the presumption may be shown to be spurious by new, and perhaps more precise, experimental data (5).

3) The insistence that scientific terms should have un-

ambiguously specifiable operational meanings serves to insure the possibility of an objective test for the hypotheses formulated by means of those terms (6). Hypotheses incapable of operational test or, rather, questions involving untestable formulations, are rejected as meaningless: "If a specific question has meaning, it must be possible to find operations by which an answer may be given to it. It will be found in many cases that the operations cannot exist, and the question therefore has no meaning." (7).

The emphasis on "operational meaning" in scientifically significant discourse has unquestionably afforded a salutary critique of certain types of procedure in philosophy and in empirical science and has provided a strong stimulus for methodological thinking. Yet, the central ideas of operational analysis as stated by their proponents are so vague that they constitute not a theory concerning the nature of scientific concepts but rather a program for the development of such a theory. They share this characteristic with the insistence of logical empiricism that all significant scientific statements must have experiential import, that the latter consists in testability by suitable data of direct observation, and that sentences which are entirely incapable of any test must be ruled out as meaningless "pseudo hypotheses." These ideas, too, constitute not so much a thesis or a theory as a program for a theory that needs to be formulated and amplified in precise terms.

An attempt to develop an operationist theory of scientific concepts will have to deal with at least two major issues: the problem of giving a more precise explication of the concept of operational definition; and the question whether operational definition in the explicated sense is indeed necessary for, and adequate to, the introduction of all nonobservational terms in empirical science.

I wish to present here in brief outline some considerations that bear on these problems. The discussion will be limited to the descriptive, or extralogical, vocabulary of empirical science and will not deal, therefore, with Bridgman's ideas on the status of logic and mathematics.

A broadened conception of operational definition and of the program of operational analysis. The terms "operational meaning" and "operational definition," as well as many of the pronouncements made in operationist writings, convey the suggestion that the criterions of application for any scientific term must ultimately refer to the outcome of some specified type of manipulation of the subject matter under investigation. Such emphasis would evidently be overly restrictive. An operational definition gives experiential meaning to the term it introduces because it enables us to decide on the applicability of that term to a given case by observing the response the case shows under specifiable test conditions. Whether these conditions can be brought about at will by "instrumental operations" or whether we have to wait for their occurrence is of great interest for the practice of scientific research, but it is inessential in securing experiential import for the defined term; what matters for this latter purpose is simply that the relevant test conditions and the requisite response be of such kind that different investigators can ascertain, by direct observation and with reasonably good agreement, whether, in a given case, the test conditions are realized and whether the characteristic response does occur.

Thus, an operational definition of the simplest kind—one that, roughly speaking, refers to instrumental operations only—will have to be construed more broadly as introducing a term by the stipulation that it is to apply to all and only those cases which, under specified observable conditions S, show a characteristic observable response R.

However, an operational definition cannot be conceived as specifying that the term in question is to apply to a given case only if S and R actually occur in that case. Physical bodies, for example, are asserted to have masses, temperatures, charges, and so on, even at times when these magnitudes are not being measured. Hence, an operational definition of a concept—such as a property or a relationship, for example—will have to be understood as ascribing the concept to all those cases that *would* exhibit the characteristic response if the test conditions *should* be realized. A concept thus characterized is clearly not "synonymous with the corresponding set of operations" (8). It constitutes not a manifest but a potential character, namely, a disposition to exhibit a certain characteristic response under specified test conditions.

But to attribute a disposition of this kind to a case in which the specified test condition is not realized (for example, to attribute solubility-in-water to a lump of sugar that is not actually put into water) is to make a generalization, and this involves an inductive risk. Thus, the application of an operationally defined term to an instance of the kind here considered would have to be adjudged "not safe" in precisely the same sense in which Bridgman insists it is "not safe" to assume that two procedures of measurement that have yielded the same results in the past will continue to do so in the future. It is now clear that if we were to reject any procedure that involves an inductive risk, we would be prevented not only from using more than one operational criterion in introducing a given term but also from ever applying a disposition term to any case in which the characteristic manifest conditions of application are not realized; thus, the use of dispositional concepts would, in effect, be prohibited.

A few remarks might be added here concerning the non-instrumental operations countenanced for the introduction especially of theoretical terms. In operationist writings, those symbolic procedures have been characterized so vaguely as to permit the introduction, by a suitable choice of "verbal" or "mental" operations, of virtually all those ideas that operational analysis was to prohibit as devoid of meaning. To meet this difficulty, Bridgman has suggested a distinction between "good" and "bad" operations (9); but he has not provided a clear criterion for this distinction. Consequently, this idea fails to plug the hole in the operationist dike.

If the principles of operationism are to admit the theoretical constructs of science but to rule out certain other kinds of terms as lacking experiential, or operational, meaning, then the vague requirement of definability by reference to instrumental and "good" symbolic operations must be replaced by a precise characterization of the kinds of sentences that may be used to introduce, or specify the meanings of, "meaningful" nonobservational terms on the basis of the observational vocabulary of science. Such a characterization would eliminate the psychologistic notion of mental operations in favor of a specification of the logico-mathematical concepts and procedures to be permitted in the context of operational definition.

The reference just made to the observational vocabulary of science is essential to the idea of operational definition; for it is in terms of this vocabulary that the test conditions and the characteristic response specified in an operational definition are described and by means of which, therefore, the meanings of operationally defined terms are ultimately characterized. Hence, the intent of the original operationist insistence on intersubjective repeatability of the defining operations will be respected if we require that the terms included in the observational vocabulary must refer to attributes (properties and relationships) that are directly and publicly observable—that is, whose presence or absence can be ascertained, under suitable conditions, by direct observation, and with good agreement among different observers (10).

In sum, then, a precise statement and elaboration of the basic tenets of operationism require an explication of the logical relationships between theoretical and observational terms, just as a precise statement and elaboration of the basic tenets of empiricism require an explication of the logical relationships connecting theoretical sentences with observation sentences describing potential data of direct observation.

Specification of meaning by explicit definition and by reduction. Initially, it may appear plausible to assume that all theoretical terms used in science can be fully defined by means of the observational vocabulary. There are various reasons, however, to doubt this assumption.

First of all, there exists a difficulty concerning the definition of the scientific terms that refer to dispositions—and, as is noted in a foregoing paragraph, all the terms introduced by operational definition have to be viewed as dispositional in character. Recent logical studies strongly suggest that dispositions can be defined by reference to manifest characteristics, such as those presented by the observational vocabulary, only with help of some "nomological modality" such as the concept of nomological truth, that is, truth by virtue of general laws of nature (11). But a concept of this kind is presumably inadmissible under operationist standards, since it is neither a directly observable characteristic nor definable in terms of such characteristics.

Another difficulty arises when we attempt to give full definitions, in terms of observables, for quantitative terms such as 'length in centimeters,' 'duration in seconds,' 'temperature in degrees Celsius.' Within scientific theory, each of these is allowed to assume any real-number value within a certain interval; and the question therefore arises whether each of the infinitely many permissible values, say of length, is capable of an operational specification of meaning. It can be shown that it is impossible to characterize every one of the permissible numerical values by some truth-functional combination of observable characteristics, since the existence of a threshold of discrimination in all areas of observation allows for only a finite number of nonequivalent combinations of this kind (*12*).

Difficulties such as these suggest the question whether it is not possible to conceive of methods more general and more flexible than definition for the introduction of scientific terms on the basis of the observational vocabulary. One such method has been developed in considerable detail by Carnap. It makes use of so-called reduction sentences, which constitute a considerably generalized version of definition sentences and are especially well suited for a precise reformulation of the intent of operational definitions. As we noted earlier, an operational definition of the simplest kind stipulates that the concept it introduces, say *C*, is to apply to those and only those cases which, under specified test conditions *S*, show a certain characteristic response *R*. In Carnap's treatment, this stipulation is replaced by the sentence

$$Sx \rightarrow (Cx \equiv Rx) \tag{1}$$

or, in words: If a case *x* satisfies the test condition *S*, then *x* is an instance of *C* if and only if *x* shows the response *R*. Formula 1, called a bilateral reduction sentence, is not a full definition (which would have to be of the form "$Cx \equiv \ldots$," with "Cx" constituting the definiendum); it specifies the meaning of "Cx," not for all cases, but only for those that satisfy the condition *S*. In this sense, it constitutes only a partial, or conditional, definition for *C* (*13*). If "*S*" and "*R*" belong to the observational vocabulary of science, formula 1 schematizes the simplest type of operational definition, which invokes (almost) exclusively instrumental operations or, better, experiential findings. Operational definitions that also utilize symbolic operations would be represented by chains of reduction sentences containing logical or mathematical symbols. Some such symbols occur even in formula 1, however; and clearly, there can be no operational definition that makes use of no logical concepts at all.

Interpretative systems. Once the idea of a partial specification of meaning is granted, it appears unnecessarily restrictive, however, to limit the sentences effecting such partial interpretation to reduction sentences in Carnap's sense. A partial specification of the meanings of a set of nonobservational terms might be expressed, more generally, by one or more sentences that connect those terms with the observational vocabulary but do not have the form of reduction sentences. And it seems well to countenance, for the same purpose, even stipulations expressed by sentences containing only nonobservational terms; for example, the stipulation that two theoretical terms are to be mutually exclusive may be regarded as a limitation and, in this sense, a partial specification of their meanings.

Generally, then, a set of one or more theoretical terms, $t_1, t_2, \ldots, t_n$, might be introduced by any set M of sentences such that (i) M contains no extralogical terms other than $t_1, t_2, \ldots, t_n$, and observation terms, (ii) M is logically consistent, and (iii) M is not equivalent to a truth of formal logic. The last two of these conditions serve merely to exclude trivial extreme cases. A set M of this kind will be referred to briefly as an *interpretative system,* its elements as *interpretative sentences.*

Explicit definitions and reduction sentences are special types of interpretative sentences, and so are the meaning postulates recently suggested by Kemeny and Carnap *(14).*

The interpretative sentences used in a given theory may be viewed simply as postulates of that theory *(15)*, with all the observation terms, as well as the terms introduced by the interpretative system, being treated as primitives. Thus construed, the specification of the meanings of nonobservational terms in science resembles what has sometimes been called the implicit definition of the primitives of an axiomatized theory by its postulates. In this latter procedure, the primitives are all uninterpreted, and the postulates then impose restrictions on any interpretation of the primitives that is to turn the postulates into true sentences. Such restrictions may be viewed as partial specifications of meaning. The use of interpretative systems as here envisaged has this distinctive peculiarity, however: the primitives include a set of terms—the observation terms—which are antecedently understood and thus not in need of any interpretation, and by reference to which the postulates effect a partial specification of meaning for the remaining, nonobservational, primitives. This partial specification again consists in limiting those interpretations of the nonobservational terms that will render the postulates true.

Implications for the idea of experiential meaning and for the distinction of analytic and synthetic sentences in science. If the introduction of nonobservational terms is conceived in this broader fashion, which appears to accord with the needs of a formal reconstruction of the langauge of empirical science, then it becomes pointless to ask for the operational definition or the experiential import of any one theoretical term. Explicit definition by means of observables is no longer generally available, and experiential—or operational—meaning can be attributed only to the set of all the nonobservational terms functioning in a given theory.

Furthermore, there remains no satisfactory general way of dividing all conceivable systems of theoretical terms into two classes: those that are scientifically significant and those that are not; those that have experiential import and those that lack it. Rather, experiential, or operational, significance appears as capable of gradations. To begin with one extreme possibility: the interpretative system M introducing the given terms may simply be a set of sentences in the form of explicit definitions that provide an observational equivalent for each of those terms. In this case, the terms introduced by M have maximal experiential significance, as it were. In another case, M might consist of reduction sentences for the theoretical terms; these will enable us to formulate, in terms of observables, a necessary and a (different) sufficient condition of application for each of the introduced terms. Again M might contain sentences in the form of definitions or reduction sentences for only some of the nonobservational terms it introduces. And finally, none of the sentences in M might have the form of a definition or of a reduction sentence; and yet, a theory whose terms are introduced by an interpretative system of this kind may well permit of test by observational findings, and in this sense, the system of its nonobservational terms may possess experiential import (16).

Thus, experiential significance presents itself as capable of degrees, and any attempt to set up a dichotomy allowing only experientially meaningful and experientially meaningless concept systems appears as too crude to be adequate for a logical analysis of scientific concepts and theories.

The use of interpretative systems is a more inclusive method of introducing theoretical terms than the method of meaning postulates developed by Carnap and Kemeny. For although meaning postulates are conceived as analytic and, hence, as implying only analytic consequences, an interpretative system may imply certain sentences that contain observation terms but no theoretical terms and are neither formal truths of logic nor analytic in the customary sense. Consider, for example, the following two interpretative sentences, which form what Carnap calls a reduction pair, and which interpret "C" by means of observation predicates, "R_1" "S_1" "R_2" "S_2":

$$S_1x \to (R_1x \to Cx) \tag{2.1}$$
$$S_2x \to (R_2x \to -Cx). \tag{2.2}$$

Since in no case the sufficient conditions for C and for $-C$ (non-C) can be satisfied jointly, the two sentences imply the consequence (17) that, for every case x,

$$-(S_1x \cdot R_1x \cdot S_2x \cdot R_2x), \tag{3}$$

that is, no case x exhibits the attributes S_1, R_1, S_2, R_2 jointly. Now, an assertion of this kind is not a truth of formal logic, nor can it generally be viewed as true solely by virtue of the meanings of its constituent terms. Carnap therefore treats this consequence of formulas 2.1 and 2.2 as empirical and as expressing the factual content of the reduction pair from which it was derived. Occurrences of this kind are by no means limited to reduction sentences, and we see that in the use of interpretative systems, specification of meaning and statement of empirical fact—two functions of language often considered as completely distinct—become so intimately bound up with each other as to raise serious doubt about the advisability or even the possibility of preserving that distinction in a logical reconstruction of science. This consideration suggests that we dispense with the distinction, so far maintained for expository purposes, between the interpretative sentences, included in M, and the balance of the sentences constituting a scientific theory: we may simply conceive of the two sets of sentences as constituting one "interpreted theory."

The results obtained in this brief analysis of the operationist view of significant scientific concepts are closely analogous to those obtainable by a similar study of the logical empiricist view of significant scientific statements, or hypotheses (*18*). In the latter case, the original requirement of full verifiability or full falsifiability by experiential data has to give way to the more liberal demand for confirmability—that is, partial verifiability. This demand can be shown to be properly applicable to entire theoretical systems rather than to individual hypotheses—a point emphasized, in effect, already by Pierre Duhem. Experiential significance is then seen to be a matter of degree, so that the originally intended sharp distinction between cognitively meaningful and cognitively meaningless hypotheses (or systems of such) has to be abandoned; and it even appears doubtful whether the distinction between analytic and synthetic sentences can be effectively maintained in a formal model of the language of empirical science.

NOTES

1. P. W. Bridgman, "Some general principles of operational analysis" and "Rejoinders and second thoughts" *Psychol. Rev.* **52**, 246 (1945); "The nature of some of our physical concepts" *Brit. J. Phil. Sci.* **1**, 258 (1951).

2. ——, "Operational analysis" *Phil. Sci.* **5**, 123 (1938); *Brit. J. Phil. Sci.* **1**, 258 (1951).

3. ——, *Phil. Sci.* **5**, 116 (1938).

4. ——, *Brit. J. Phil. Sci.* **1**, 260 (1951).

5. ——, *The Logic of Modern Physics* (Macmillan, New York, 1927), pp. 6, 23–24; *Phil. Sci.* **5**, 121 (1938); *Psychol. Rev.* **52**, 247 (1945); "The operational aspect of meaning," *Synthése* **8**, 255 (1950–51).

6. ——, *Psychol. Rev.* **52**, 246 (1945).

7. ——, *The Logic of Modern Physics*, p. 28.

8. ——, *ibid.*, p. 5; qualified by Bridgman's reply [*Phil. Sci.* **5**, 117 (1938)] to R. B. Lindsay, "A critique of operationalism in physics," *Phil. Sci.* **4**, (1937), a qualification that was essentially on the ground, quite different from that given in the present paper, that operational meaning is only a necessary, but presumably not a sufficient, characteristic of scientific concepts.

9. ——, *Phil. Sci.* **5**, 126 (1938); "Some implications of recent points of view in physics," *Rev. intern. phil.* **3**, 484 (1949). The intended distinction between good and bad operations is further obscured by the fact that in Bridgman's discussion the meaning of "good operation" shifts from what might be described as

"operation whose use in operational definition insures experiential meaning and testability" to "scientific procedure—in some very broad sense—which leads us to correct predictions."

10. The condition thus imposed upon the observational vocabulary of science is of a pragmatic character; it demands that each term included in that vocabulary be of such a kind that under suitable conditions, different observers can, by means of direct observation, arrive at a high degree of agreement on whether the term applies to a given situation. The expression 'coincides with' as applicable to instrument needles and marks on scales of instruments is an example of a term meeting this condition. That human beings are capable of developing observational vocabularies that satisfy the given requirement is a fortunate circumstance: without it, science as an intersubjective enterprise would be impossible.

11. To illustrate briefly, it seems reasonable, *prima facie*, to define 'x is soluble in water' by 'if x is put in water then x dissolves.' But if the phrase 'if . . . then . . .' is here construed as the truth-functional, or "material," conditional, then the objects qualified as soluble by the definition include, among others, all those things that are never put in water—no matter whether or not they are actually soluble in water. This consequence—one aspect of the "paradoxes of material implication"—can be avoided only if the aforementioned definiens is construed in a more restrictive fashion. The idea suggests itself to construe 'x is soluble in water' as short for 'by virtue of some general laws of nature, x dissolves if x is put in water,' or briefly, 'it is nomologically true that if x is put in water then x dissolves.' The phrase 'if . . . then . . .' may now be understood in the truth-functional sense again. However, the acceptability of this analysis depends, of course, upon whether nomological truth can be considered as a sufficiently clear concept. For a fuller discussion of this problem complex, see especially R. Carnap, "Testability and meaning," *Phil. Sci.* 3 (1936) and 4 (1937) and N. Goodman, "The problem of counterfactual conditionals," *J. Phil.* 44 (1947).

12. In other words, it is not possible to provide, for every theoretically permissible value r of the length $l(x)$ of a rod x, a definition of the form

$$[l(x) = r] =_{df} C(P_1x, P_2x, \ldots , P_nx),$$

where $P_1, P_2, \ldots , P_n$ are observable characteristics, and the definiens is an expression formed from 'P_1x', 'P_2x', . . . , 'P_nx' with help of the connective words 'and,' 'or,' and 'not' alone.

It is worth noting, however, that if the logical constants allowed in the definiens include, in addition to truth-functional connectives, also quantifiers and the identity sign, then a finite observational vocabulary may permit the explicit definition of a denumerable infinity of further terms. For instance, if 'x spatially contains y' and 'y is an apple' are included in the observational vocabulary, then it is possible to define the expressions 'x contains 0 apples,' 'x contains exactly 1 apple,' 'x contains exactly 2 apples,' and so forth, in a manner familiar from the Frege-Russell construction of arithmetic out of logic. Yet even if definitions of this type are countenanced—and no doubt they are in accord with the intent of operationist analysis— there remain serious obstacles for an operationist account of the totality of real numbers which are permitted as theoretical values of length, mass, and so forth. On this point, see C. G. Hempel, *Fundamentals of Concept Formation in Empirical Science* (Univ. of Chicago Press, Chicago, 1952), sec. 7. Gustav Bergmann, in his contribution to the present symposium, deplores this argument—although he agrees with its point—on the ground that it focuses attention on a characteristic shared by all quantitative concepts instead of bringing out the differences between, say, length and the psi-function. He thinks this regrettable because, after all, as he puts it, "the real numbers are merely a part of the logical apparatus; concept formation is a matter of the descriptive vocabulary." I cannot accept the suggestion conveyed by this statement. To be sure, the theory of real numbers can be developed as a branch (or as an extension) of logic; however, my argument concerns not the definability of real numbers in logical terms, but the possibility of formulating an observational equivalent for each of the infinitely many permissible real-number values of length, temperature, and so forth. And this is clearly a question concerning the descriptive vocabulary rather than merely the logical apparatus of empirical science. I quite agree with Bergmann, however, that it would be of considerable interest to explicate whatever logical differences may obtain between quantitative concepts which, intuitively speaking, exhibit different degrees of theoretical abstractness, such as length on the one hand and the psi-function on the other.

13. The use of reduction sentences circumvents one of the difficulties encountered in the attempt to give explicit and, thus, complete definitions of disposition terms: the conditional and biconditional signs occurring in formula 1 may be construed truth-functionally without giving rise to undesirable consequences of the kind characterized in reference *11*. For details, see R. Carnap, "Testability and meaning," *Phil. Sci.* (1936–37), pt. II; also C. G. Hempel, *Fundamentals of Concept Formation in Empirical Science,* secs. 6 and 8. Incidentally, the use of nomological concepts is not entirely avoided in Carnap's procedure; the reduction sentences that are permitted for the introduction of new terms are required to satisfy certain conditions of logical or of nomological validity. See R. Carnap, *Phil. Sci.* **3** and **4** (1936–37), pp. 442–443.

14. J. G. Kemeny, "Extension of the methods of inductive logic," *Philosophical Studies* **3** (1952); R. Carnap, "Meaning postulates," *ibid.* **3** (1952).

15. For the case of Carnap's reduction sentences, the postulational interpretation was suggested to me by N. Goodman and by A. Church.

16. This is illustrated by the following simple model case: The theory T consists of the sentence '$(x) ((C_1x . C_2x) \rightarrow C_3x)$' and its logical consequences; the three "theoretical" terms occurring in it are introduced by the interpretative set M consisting of the sentences '$O_1x \rightarrow (C_1x . C_2x)$' and '$(C_1x . C_3x) \rightarrow (O_2x \vee O_3x)$,' where '$O_1$,' '$O_2$,' '$O_3$,' belong to the observational vocabulary. As is readily seen, T permits, by virtue of M, the "prediction" that if an object has the observable property O_1 but lacks the observable property O_2, then it will have the observable property O_3. Thus T is susceptible to experiential test, although M provides for none of its constituent terms both a necessary and a sufficient observational, or operational, criterion of application.

17. Carnap calls it the representative sentence of the pair of formulas 2.1 and 2.2. See R. Carnap, *Phil. Sci.* **3** and **4** (1936–37), p. 444 and p. 451. Generally, when a term is introduced by several reduction sentences representing different operational criterions of application, then the agreement among the results of the corresponding procedures, which must be presupposed if the reduction sentences are all to be compatible with one another, is expressed by the representative sentence associated with the given set of reduction sentences. The representative sentence reflects, therefore, the inductive risk which, as Bridgman has stressed, is incurred by using more than one operational criterion for a given term.

18. C. G. Hempel, "Problems and changes in the empiricist criterion of meaning," *Rev. intern. phil.* **4** (1951), and "The concept of cognitive significance: a reconsideration," *Proc. Am. Acad. Arts Sci.* **80** (1951): W. V. Quine, "Two dogmas of empiricism," *Phil. Rev.* **40** (1951).

Operationalism in Physics

by R. B. Lindsay

IT IS scarcely necessary to emphasize the important role that the operational idea, as suggested and developed by P. W. Bridgman, has played in *physical* methodology during the past quarter-century. A token of its lively character is the fact that it can provide the background of a general symposium for the reassessment of the place of operationalism in philosophy as well as in physics. Many physical methodological points of view—for instance, Ostwald's energetics—arise, produce interest and excitement, have their day, and then are duly embalmed and laid away in the limbo of forgotten things. But Bridgman's ideas still challenge the attention of both scientists and scholars in many fields.

Before embarking on another critique, it may be worth while to indulge in a brief review of the historical situation; even if incomplete, this will in any event set the stage for the questions that I personally desire to raise.

Bridgman's stress on the value of the operational point of view was first brought widely to public notice in his book *The Logic of Modern Physics* (1927). His views were further developed in "A physicist's second reaction to Mengenlehre" [*Scripta Math.* **2**, 101, 224, (1934)] and in the later book *The Nature of Physical Theory* (1936). He never claimed that the idea was original with him and, indeed, in his first introduction of the notion stressed the essentially operational character of Einstein's treatment of the concepts of space and time in the relativity of inertial systems. Actually vestiges of the point of view, naturally not usually presented in the language Bridgman prefers to employ, may be found scattered throughout earlier literature on physical theorizing, as for instance in Galileo's *Two New Sciences*—recall his attempt to describe to his skeptical contemporaries the meaning and value of the concept of variable instantaneous velocity—or, to mention only two other examples, in the writings of Helmholtz on non-Euclidean geometry and those of W. K. Clifford on the concepts of space and time.

In essence what Bridgman was driving at can best be described in his own words, taken from a relatively recent publication (*1*):

The fundamental idea back of an operational analysis is . . . that we do not know the meaning of a concept unless we can specify the operations which were used by us or our neighbor in applying the concept in any concrete situation.

It should at once be remarked that the author of this statement apparently at no time ever contemplated the foun-

lation of a *new* philosophy of physics to be called *operationalism*. Actually he has shied away from this term and
has preferred to speak and write merely of "operational
analysis" or the operational point of view. When, however,
one stresses with such emphasis a methodological technique
of this kind, one must expect that it will gain attention, and
Bridgman's views certainly have achieved this! It was probably inevitable that they would also suffer misinterpretation.
In his anxiety to stress the operational technique as the only
sure way of avoiding inconsistencies and contradictions in
the use of physical concepts, it was perhaps natural to over-
stress the significance of actual physical operations in the
laboratory. Many were misled into thinking that these were
the only operations that Bridgman wished to tolerate and
some critiques followed. At least one of these played devil's
advocate in such thoroughgoing fashion that Bridgman
wrote a reply ["Operational analysis," *Philosophy of Science* 5, 114 (1938)] in which he cleared up doubtful points
by explicitly including "paper-and-pencil" operations to
cover many of the concepts constructed in the building of
physical theories. He also conceded that the theory builder
should be allowed all the latitude he wishes in these "intermediate constructions," provided only that "the ultimate
outcome of the theory be expressible in terms of operations
applicable in the concrete situation." I assume we may take
this to mean that physical theorizing (if pursued with logical
consistency) is free of all restrictions save only that ultimately the results must be identifiable with laboratory operations and testable through their agreement or disagreement with the latter.

No theoretical physicist could, I believe, disagree with the
foregoing interpretation of physical operationalism. One
would have therefore supposed that the whole question
might be considered closed, so far as physics is concerned.
This was my view at that time (1938). It was therefore with
great interest and not a little surprise that I studied the more
recently published collection of papers *The Nature of Some
of Our Physical Concepts,* Philosophical Library, New
York, 1952, which were originally presented by Bridgman
as lectures at University College in the University of London
in 1950. Here the operational idea is applied in fascinating
fashion to such concepts as field, action at a distance, heat,
and entropy. Once more the distinction between "paper-

and-pencil" and "instrumental" operations is clearly brought out, and the allowability of both kinds is admitted. But, as I read the discussion, there emerged a question that somehow the papers did not settle in my mind: How much latitude will Bridgman allow to the "free construction" of concepts? Although it is always a bit dangerous to quote out of context, the passage that particularly concerned me is this:

It will be seen that a very great latitude is allowed to the verbal and the paper-and-pencil operation. I think, however, that physicists are agreed in imposing one restriction on the freedom of such operations, namely, that such operations must be capable of eventually, although perhaps indirectly, making connection with instrumental operations.

I do not know how to interpret this in any other way than that the author believes that ultimately the concepts and postulates of every successful physical theory shall be instrumentally verifiable. Admittedly the phrase "although perhaps indirectly" needs clarification. This then sets up the question I wish to ask Bridgman. Here lies actually the principal purpose of the present paper.

At this point perhaps it may be well to review briefly my own conception of physical explanation, which, so far as I know, is that of most theoretical physicists, although each man's phrasing is his own and there are always differences in emphasis at various points. Physical explanation ultimately is essentially deductive in character, consisting of theories whose aim is to predict the physical laws that describe physical experience. A physical theory starts with primitive, undefined concepts, such as the notions of space and time. It proceeds to the construction of more precisely defined constructs, for instance, mass and force in mechanics, into whose definition there enter both epistemic (operational) and constitutive (theoretical) characteristics. These aspects of the definition of physical constructs have been rather fully set forth by Henry Margenau (2) and will not be further elaborated at this point. The next step is the postulation of relationships connecting the constructs (for example, the principles of mechanics, like $F = ma$). Next in order are logical deductions by appropriate mathematical manipulation of relationships among quantities all of which have sufficient epistemic significance to be measurable in the laboratory. If these relationships are sufficiently general in character, they are called *physical laws* (for example, the law for freely falling bodies $s = \frac{1}{2} gt^2$); that is, they are supposed to describe adequately routines or patterns of physical experience. The final stage is the laboratory test of the law and its verification or refutation.

Clearly the operational viewpoint enters significantly on the *instrumental* level into two steps of the logical scheme just set forth: (i) in the definition of appropriate and useful instrumental constructs for describing physical experience, and (ii) in the laboratory testing of the consequences of the postulates of the theory expressed in terms of relationships connecting such constructs. The operational viewpoint enters on the "paper-and-pencil" level in the introduction of theoretical constructs as, for example, the velocity of any particular single molecule in kinetic theory, or the velocity of a single electron in atomic theory, or the state function (ψ function) in quantum mechanics. It also enters in the postulates or hypotheses of the theory which, though often suggested by experience, are essentially and in the last analysis free creations of the human mind.

It is just at this point that I should like to raise a question. Does the thoroughgoing operationalist (I dislike this term just as much as Bridgman does but see no simple alternative to its use in this context) require that before a physical theory can be considered a really satisfactory explanation of physical experience, instrumental interpretation or validation must be given to every element in the theory?

It seems to me that the whole history of physics exhibits the impracticability of this demand. If we examine critically the postulates of what are now called the classical physical theories, we find that even though the inventors may have wished to base their hypotheses more or less directly on experience and at times may indeed have thought that they were doing so, there nevertheless inheres an ideal element in all these postulates, not accessible to experiment except through the special cases that result as logical deductions of the general principles. I suppose we all admit that Galileo took a commonsense approach to the problem of motion. At least it seems common sense to us today, although it did not seem so to most of his contemporaries. Yet his boldness in constructing out of his head the concepts of instantaneous velocity and acceleration, and showing that certain simple assumptions connected with them lead by direct mathematical deduction to the observed laws of falling bodies, justifies his position as the creator of theoretical physics. In more recent times physicists have not hesitated to call on their creative imagination for constructs like, say, Planck's quantum of action that have no direct connection with experience but whose unifying influence on large domains of physical phenomena has been considered ample justification for their postulation.

Now possibly this procedure of free imaginative construction has not been good physical methodology, but most physicists admit that it has worked pretty well, and the fact that the concepts have in most cases been of the paper-and-pencil variety has not prevented their successful employment. In this process there has admittedly been little assurance of the association of *truth* in the philosophic sense with physical concepts and postulates, but I think physicists have learned to eschew this rather illusive goal in favor of the more pragmatic one of *success* in subsuming large areas of experience and in predicting hitherto unobserved phenomena. But we should not forget that there are other criterions of the value of physical theories not to be despised, among them, for example, simplicity of formulation, esthetic appeal, and teachability to others. These have been sufficiently stressed elsewhere to need no further elaboration here.

I am puzzled by the phrase "although perhaps indirectly" in the quotation I just made from Bridgman. Perhaps this is the nub of my difficulty. If indeed by indirect connection of the postulates with experience one means simply that their logically deduced consequences can be instrumentally verified, then there is no problem; but somehow I find it hard to believe that this is what Bridgman means, since in a later part of the same paper he takes some pains to analyze and compare the action-at-a-distance (particle) and the field constructs from the standpoint of their instrumental connotations. Concerning himself with the rather well-known fact that both constructs can be made to lead to similar consequences in problems in mechanics and electricity, he reaches the conclusion that "there is no way by which the desired distinction between action at a distance and action by a field can be given instrumental significance." I cannot imagine that he would have devoted so much time to this discussion had he not attached significance to the desirable possibility of distinguishing between the two theoretical points of view by direct instrumental means. The inability to produce this distinction does not make me so unhappy as it apparently does the holder of the thoroughgoing operational point of view, since it seems to me that in the development of physics we must be constantly on the watch for different constructs and postulational systems. In fact, the continual creation of physical experience that is going on in physical laboratories renders this imperative, if the job of physical explanation is to keep pace with physical discovery.

One wonders whether the desire of the operationalist to subject the postulational structure of physical theories to direct instrumental test may reflect a conscious or unconscious feeling on his part that there exists some ultimately valid and verified explanation of all physical experience or, to put it in words often used, although to me they are meaningless, that there exists an ultimately *true* representation of *reality?* Probably I am an incorrigible conventionalist, but to me this viewpoint is illusory and has little to do with the success of physics as a science. If it really helped us forward in the search for better explanations, as a pragmatist I should not hesitate to endorse it enthusiastically. Unfortunately I can find no warrant for this belief. To me the future of physical theory lies in the bold use of imagination. No one knows whence the successful ideas will come, but no one can reasonably doubt that they *will* come in the future as they have in the past.

NOTES

1. "The nature of some of our physical concepts," *Brit. J. for the Philosophy of Science* **1**, 257 (1951).
2. *The Nature of Physical Reality* (McGraw-Hill, New York, 1950), pp. 220ff.

The Present State of Operationalism

by P. W. Bridgman

THERE WOULD SEEM to be no reason why I am better fitted than anyone else to open this discussion. As I listened to the papers I felt that I have only a historical connection with this thing called "operationalism." In short, I feel that I have created a Frankenstein, which has certainly got away from me. I abhor the word *operationalism* or *operationism,* which seems to imply a dogma, or at least a thesis of some kind. The thing I have envisaged is too simple to be dignified by so pretentious a name; rather, it is an attitude or point of view generated by continued practice of operational analysis. So far as any dogma is involved here at all, it is merely the conviction that it is better, because it takes us further, to analyze into doings or happenings rather than into objects or entities.

What I conceive to be involved here may be a little clearer if the historical background is understood, and I hope you will pardon me if I interject some personal remarks. The date usually associated with this is 1927, the year of the publication of my book *The Logic of Modern Physics,* but preparation for this in my own thinking went back at least to 1914, when the task of giving two advanced courses in electrodynamics was suddenly thrust upon me. Included in these courses was material from the restricted theory of relativity. The underlying conceptual situation in this whole area seemed very obscure to me and caused me much intellectual distress, which I tried to alleviate as best I could. Another cause of distress was the situation in dimensional analysis, which at that time was often so expounded as to raise doubt whether experimental work was really necessary at all. The dimensional situation proved comparatively simple, and I was able to think the situation through to my own satisfaction—an experience that perceptibly increased my intellectual morale. The analysis, which was essentially operational, although the word was not used, was published in 1922 (*Dimensional Analysis,* Yale Univ. Press). I think the word *operation* was first explicitly used in a discussion that I gave at the Boston meeting of the AAAS in 1923 at a symposium on relativity theory participated in by George Birkhoff, Harlow Shapley, and myself.

The Logic of Modern Physics was written during a half sabbatical in 1926 under a stringent time limit, for I knew that at the end of September my laboratory would reabsorb me. In view of this time limit, I had to map out the questions that to me appeared most pressing and to be satisfied with discussions of which I could say "at least this much must be true and be part of the final picture," and not attempt the more ambitious program of a complete analysis. In short, I was compelled to be satisfied with a "necessary" as opposed to a "sufficient" analysis. A great many interesting and important leads had to be left unexplored: for example, an analysis of what it is that makes an operation suitable for the formulation of a scientific concept; again, in what terms can operations be specified. It has, in fact, been a surprise to me that, since the publication of my book, so much of the concern of others has been with abstract methodological questions suggested by the endeavor to erect some sort of a philosophic system rather than with attempts to follow the more concrete and obvious leads.

Since writing the book, I have never again been able to devote as sustained attention to this field but have had to content myself with shorter excursion, resulting in a number of articles and a couple of thin books. But at the same time, with the continued practice of operational analysis, my ideas have been changing and growing and gaining in generality. If I were to start today to expound my attitude systematically, the order of presentation would be different. The general points of view would be presented earlier in the treatment, with, I think, avoidance of much confusion. It is often thought that there is a normative aspect to "operationalism," which is understood as the dogma that definitions *should* be formulated in terms of operations. As I see it, there is in the *general* point of view nothing normative whatever. An operational analysis is always possible, that is, an analysis into what was done or what happened. An operational analysis can be given of the most obscurely metaphysical definition, such as Newton's definition of absolute time as that which flows by itself uniformly and equably. What is more, any person can make an operational analysis, whether or not he accepts what he supposes to be the thesis of "operationalism," and whether or not he thinks he is wasting his time in so doing. So far as the "operationalist" is to be distinguished from the "nonoperationalist," it is in the conviction of the former that it is often profitable and clarifying to make an operational analysis, and also, I suspect, in his private feeling that often the "nonoperationalist" does not want to make an operational analysis through fear that it might result in a change in his attitude.

If one has consistently used operational analysis, I think one's general point of view comes to acquire a certain flavor and certain considerations come to be emphasized in his thinking; these I shall endeavor to characterize briefly. In the first place, one is impressed by the observation that operational analysis can always be pushed to the point where sharpness disappears. The "yes or no" signal of recent information theory, the "all or none" firing of a neurone of the physiologist, and so on, lose their sharpness when considered as processes occurring in time, and the operations of logic lose their sharpness when the analysis is pushed to the point of self-doubt. Again, one is impressed by the complexity of the verbal structure that mankind has erected through the ages. Here is an autonomous world in which a man can, and frequently does, live a more or less self-contained and independent existence. On the other hand, despite the complexity of the verbal world, the external world of objects and happenings is inconceivably more complex—so complex that all aspects of it can never be reproduced by any verbal structure. Even in physics this is not sufficiently appreciated, as is shown, for example, by the reification of energy. The totality of situations covered by various aspects of the energy concept is too complex to be reproduced by any simple verbal device. As a corollary of the continued interplay of the verbal and the "objective" worlds, I personally have come to feel the value of analyzing our operations as far as possible into their "instrumental" and "paper-and-pencil" components and think there is much here that is still unexplored. I think there is much to be done in non-scientific fields along these lines. For instance, I anticipate that many of the operations of philosophy will be found to be essentially verbal and incapable of being made to emerge into the instrumental world. I believe that revolutionary results will follow a full realization of the inescapability and immanence of the element of human enterprise.

Turning now to a consideration of a couple of the points raised by the preceding papers, I am not particularly disturbed by the fact that it is sometimes difficult to fit the apparent demands of "operationalism" into a logically complete and satisfactory scheme. Part of this failure I think arises from misconception of what is involved; but in any event, as I have already intimated, I would expect that the analysis could be pushed so far that it would become unsatisfactory logically. That this should be possible appears to me to be fully as much a commentary on the nature of logic as on the nature of "operationalism." At the same time, I fully agree with Hempel that there is much unnecessary vagueness in such matters, as for example, in the answer to the question of what it is that makes an operation "good" for the purposes of the scientist. There is certainly much room for improvement here, and I think the improvement will be naturally forthcoming when the operational point of view has reached a higher state of development than at present.

With regard to Lindsay's question concerning my meaning in saying that it is desirable that the paper-and-pencil operations of the theorist be capable of eventual contact, *although perhaps indirectly,* with instrumental operations, I shall answer by giving two examples. The first is concerned with the stress at any interior point of a solid body exposed to external forces. This stress is a complex of six components, constructed by the theoretical physicist and incapable of measurement by any instrument, if for no other reason than that the interior points of a solid body are inaccessible. However, the stress is connected through the equations of elasticity theory with the forces acting upon the free faces, and these forces have immediate instrumental significance. Here, what I meant by an "indirect" connection is the connection through the equations of elasticity. Again, the psi function of wave mechanics, defined as a probability amplitude, is at first a pure construction of the theoretical physicist, but again it makes connection through mathematical operations, in this case operations of integration, with the mean density of electric charge, which does have instrumental significance.

With regard to my concern to show that there can be no instrumental distinction between action at a distance and action through a field, I did not feel badly about the discovery, as Lindsay inferred from my, I fear, obscure exposition. On the contrary, I felt much pleased with myself, because my reading of scientific literature had led me to suppose that most physicists assume that there is some essential "physical" difference between these two points of view. In showing that this distinction is on the "paper-and-pencil" level, I thought that I was really saying something. In general, I think that there need be no qualms that the operational point of view will ever place the slightest restriction on the freedom of the theoretical physicist to explore the consequences of any free mental construction that he is ingenious enough to make. It must be remembered that the operational point of view suggested itself from observation of physicists in action.

Beyond Operationalism

by Raymond J. Seeger

THESE REMARKS are concerned specifically with R. B. Lindsay's present paper on "Operationalism in physics" and more generally with P. W. Bridgman's 1950 lectures on the "Nature of some of our physical concepts."

As a fellow-student of Henry Margenau in a Yale class under Lindsay, I learned long ago to appreciate the economic clarification of physical concepts revealed by the positivist's (Mach, 1) point of view. At the same time, however, I was introduced to the creative value of the conventionalist's (Poincaré, 2) outlook. The customary interplay, however, of irreducible data and of thoughtful theory is itself a third factor that must not be ignored. Without some heuristic presuppositions I find that consistent operationalism is not pregnant theoretically, and without some faithful generalizations I find that thoroughgoing operationalism is not satisfactory intellectually. For me it has primarily pragmatic, but necessarily incomplete, values. As Planck (3) has emphasized, the laws of nature are not solely the inventions of man. In man's formulation of them, however, there is always something of himself; man's imprint is upon nature —but nature is there first.

The day before Christmas my little girl asked, "Daddy, do you believe in Santa Claus?" Restless the Christmas Eve sleep of a Scrooge who does not believe in Santa Claus! As we grow older a more meaningful question emerges: "What do you believe about Santa Claus, that jovial spirit of Christmas?" So, too, one may start initially with the immature question: "Do you believe in the operational point of view in physics? in operationalism, in general?" Inevitably, one is forced later to consider more precisely what one does believe. Granted that the final statements of physical theory must be operational in character in order that they may be checked with natural phenomena, what about the initial axioms? Can first principles, indeed, conceivably be operational, say, the inertial principle of classical mechanics or the state ψ functions of quantum mechanics? Then, too, what about intermediate statements? Must each step of a deductive approach itself be term-wise operational? If not, where does one draw the line between theoretical statements that are operational and those that are not? If there is a criterion, must it, too, be operational? It seems to me that not every operational statement is necessarily meaningful and that not every nonoperational statement is necessarily meaningless. For example, a conception, like a chimera, may have operational components but no composite meaning.

We have been socially urged to speak "the truth, the whole truth, and nothing but the truth." A scientific statement, however, may be true to certain observed facts, but not true to others. For example, someone remarks, "He was a lion in the fight." Is this statement true? As far as a certain quality describing participation in the fight is concerned, yes! Yet no one is so misled by the metaphor as to picture a real lion in the ring. On the contrary, progress in science has often been facilitated by the use of an analogy. For example, despite general acceptance of the kinetic theory of matter, physicists still find the concept of a mechanical continuum useful in describing the physical properties of fluids. In the case of analogy we may even form Grecian monsters, like all-seeing Argus, to emphasize certain characteristics. In this respect the image is true to certain aspects, but it does not portray nothing but the truth. Herein lies the danger! We may take our picture too seriously—we may persuade ourselves that the whole is true. A critical operational viewpoint would rightly prevent any such false impressions.

At the same time, however, by its minimal principle of economy, dogmatic operationalism may curb enthusiastic creativity. It places a premium upon economic description (Kirchhoff, 4) without insuring imaginative prediction (Hertz, 5), not to mention esthetic values. The former favors a completed theory; the latter, an evolving one. In the incipient stages of development, adequacy of expression may be more important than economy of thought. You ask me: "What is x?" Usually, I reply: "It is like this—but it is not exactly this." "It is like that—but it is not precisely that." (In this connection, recall the early interpretations of the unknown x-rays.) Simplicity as the primary criterion for systematizing data may be misleading if the data are incomplete. A classical example of this reactionary spirit is Mach's own antipathy to atomism with its sterile outcome.

There is no *a priori* reason, moreover, for expecting that the best form of descriptive theory can simultaneously provide predictability. For example, the esthetic appearance of a completed building may no longer reveal the crude outline of a simple scaffolding used in the construction. Thus, the simple theory of the Bohr atom might have been missed if one had to formulate first the more elaborate theory of quantum mechanics to comprehend not only the Balmer spectral lines but also multiplet and hyperfine structure, the Zeeman and the Stark effects. Too many details may fog the main outline. The finalistic operational world-view, indeed, may not be the best possible theoretical world in the making. A less logical picture, or even several possible world-constructs may be more heuristically valuable.

One further note of caution about dogmatism with respect to operationalism! It is conceivable that the developing world-picture, which we find to be increasingly true to observed data and believe to be made somewhat in our own intellectual image, may be real (in the everyday usage of that word). However arbitrary the description by an observer who cannot be completely detached from a phenomenon, there is an ever-growing body of physical measurements that can be reproduced independently of any one observer. We become more understandingly aware of the workings of a world outside ourselves, even though we may never attain direct and complete understanding of it. The relativism of our views may only distort an absolute object. Science, I believe, is more than a grinning (mocking) Cheshire cat.

My underlining of Lindsay's chief criticism of thorough-going operationalism is best summed up, I believe, in the concluding (appendix) statement of Max Born (6): "Faith, imagination, and intuition are decisive factors in the progress of science as in any other human activity." We must go beyond operationalism! At the same time, however, despite Lindsay's own preference, I personally hope that we can go beyond conventionalism!

NOTES

1. E. Mach, *The Science of Mechanics* (Open Court, ed., 5, 1942); E. Mach, *Analysis of Sensations* (Open Court, 1914); R. von Mises, *Positivism* (Harvard Univ. Press, Cambridge, Mass., 1951).
2. H. Poincaré, *The Foundations of Science* (Science Press, New York, 1913).
3. M. Planck, *Scientific Autobiography* (Philosophical Library, New York, 1949).
4. G. Kirchhoff, *Vorlesungen über mathematische Physik: Mechanik* (B. G. Teubner, Leipzig, 1876).
5. H. Hertz, *Principles of Mechanics* (Macmillan, London-New York, 1899).
6. M. Born, *Natural Philosophy of Cause and Chance* (Oxford Univ. Press, London, 1949).

Operationism and Relativity

by Adolf Grünbaum

AGAIN AND AGAIN P. W. Bridgman has told us that the restricted theory of relativity was at once the foundation and the inspiration of his espousal of the operational point of view (*1*). Since earlier critiques of operationism by other authors seem not to have contested Bridgman's invocation of relativity theory, I wish to explain here (i) why I cannot accept his philosophic interpretation of the restricted theory of relativity, and (ii) why I maintain that he is not entitled to rely on Einstein's analysis of space and time for support of his views.

Before considering relativity, it is necessary to articulate operationism in terms of distinctions that are familiar from the general theory of signs. Students of semiotic have found that it is both valid and important to distinguish between pragmatics and semantics when giving an account of an interpreted system of signs such as physical theory. It is admittedly illuminating to study psychologically, sociologically, and otherwise the activities of scientists in their pursuit of science and to investigate the relationships between scientific symbols and their human users. Studies of this kind constitute the field of pragmatics. But, from the standpoint of the *logic* of physics, our concern must be *not* with pragmatics but rather with the relationships between physical theory on the one hand and the designata or denotata of that theory in the realm of nature on the other. In this sense then, the logic of physics is the semantics of physical theory. Now, it seems to me that, fundamentally, Bridgman's thesis is that the distinction between pragmatics and semantics is illegitimate and unfounded, semantics being properly a mere part of pragmatics. For he writes (2):

What now is the criterion that the meaning of a term in isolation is known? Here again [that is, just as in the case of effective communications, taken as a whole] the criterion can be formulated in terms of action. If I know what it was that my fellow did to decide to use the term, or if my fellow can reconstruct for himself what it was that I did in deciding to use the term, then, I think we must say that the meaning of the term in that particular usage is fixed. . . . We see, therefore, that a specification of meanings, both of isolated terms and of communication in toto, involves a specification of action of some sort.

No one will wish to deny that a study of the activities of scientists should comprise their work-behavior in the laboratory as well as their work with mathematical and linguistic symbols. But the objects that physics talks about are neither the manual nor the conceptual activities of physicists; instead, physics is concerned with the postulational and observational ascertainment of the attributes and relationships that characterize various kinds of physical entities and processes. These latter entities and processes are the objects or designata of both classical and quantum physics. For, as H. Reichenbach has justly pointed out (3):

Like all other parts of physics, quantum mechanics deals with nothing but relations between physical things; all its statements can be made without reference to an observer. The disturbance by the means of observation—which is certainly one of the basic facts asserted in quantum mechanics—is an entirely physical affair which does not include any reference to effects emanating from human beings as observers. [p. 15] . . . The instrument of measurement disturbs, not because it is an instrument used by human observers, but because it is a physical thing like all other physical things [p. 17].

Accordingly, I do not see how Bridgman can escape the charge that he is gratuitously absorbing semantics within pragmatics. Once we recognize, however, that he regards this absorption as fully justified, we can readily understand why he writes as follows (4):

The presence of an operational component in any analysis of concepts seems to me to be a simple result of observation and not to be a matter for argument. It is doubtless more usual to attempt an analysis in terms of objects of the external world or in terms of fixed and static elements of other sorts. But when I ask myself what I mean when I say that objects exist, or that there is an external world, the only answer that I can give is in terms of activities of one sort or another.

Furthermore, we can now see why he is led to give a psychologistic account of the logical nerve of deductive inference, an account that implicitly denies Frege's distinction between the context of justification and the context of discovery (5). And it is therefore not at all surprising that Bridgman's analysis of the restricted theory of relativity will exhibit the defects of his thesis with particular clarity, as I shall now endeavor to show.

The following are the results of the relativistic space-time analysis pertaining to the issue before us: any two physical events, whether we happen to observe them or not, sustain the objective temporal relationship of "later" or "earlier," if it is physically possible that they be the termini of a causal influence chain. I deliberately do not speak of connectibility via signal transmission, since such a formulation may suggest misleadingly that essential reference is made to some human dispatcher of the signal who wishes to use the signal as a means of communication with other human beings.

Mehlberg, Zilsel, and Denbigh have demonstrated convincingly (6) that *without* invoking the entropy increase, this causal theory of time does *not* succeed in providing a criterion for the unidirectionality of time, but I have shown elsewhere (6) that the entropy criterion need *not* require recourse to man's subjective sense of time-direction or to human activities, as Bridgman claims (6).

The relevant crucial difference between the Newtonian and relativistic accounts of time derives from the following fact: although pre-Einstein physics had postulated the existence of arbitrarily fast causal chains, including some of infinite velocity, the experimental work of W. Kaufmann and others persuaded Einstein to postulate that electromagnetic processes are the fastest causal chains in nature. Accordingly, in the Newtonian theory, every two events of nature stand in a determinate, unambiguous temporal relationship to each other: either they can be the termini only of causal chains of *infinite* velocity, as in the case of gravitational action-at-a-distance, or they will be the termini of causal chains of finite velocity, however large. In the former case they are absolutely simultaneous and in the latter absolutely nonsimultaneous. In restricted relativity, on the other hand, no influences can propagate themselves faster than light, and therefore every class of physical events in which each member sustains an objective relationship of temporal order to every other member will be only a proper subclass of the totality of physical events. There will be pairs of physical events whose members cannot be the termini of any influence chain and, therefore, are not related temporally by any objective criterion. But clearly the relationships between the events that *are* the termini of physically possible influence chains are *not* generated by the operations performed by human beings and do not depend in any way upon the activities of human beings or upon their presence in the cosmos. The human element does not enter until a symbolic description of these objective time relationships is given—that is, until we assign numerical *names* to these events. This assignment of names is made in such a way that the names or (time)-coordinates are indicative of the objective (temporal) relationships between the events in question as well as of certain conventions. In the case of the events that are *not* temporally related objectively, there is no nomological restriction on the names or time-coordinates to be assigned, and then the description can be governed by considerations of mathematical convenience. In particular, here is the source of the relativity of distant simultaneity and of the need for introducing a stipulation as to which particular pairs of such events will be called "simultaneous." Whatever may have been Einstein's conceptual orientation when he first made his analysis of distant simultaneity, the systematic import of that analysis relevant here is that nature permits greater latitude for the consistent assignment of numerical *names* to physical events than was thought permissible in classical physics. But apart from this somewhat greater freedom of naming, the relativistic temporal order of nature neither is generated by, nor derives its meaning from, *our* hypothetical or actual signaling activities or from any other operations performed by human beings, much as our operations of measurement are indispensable for *discovering* or *knowing* that temporal order. It is because no relations of absolute simultaneity *exist* to be measured that *our* measurements cannot disclose them; it is *not* the mere failure of *our* measurements to disclose them that *constitutes* their nonexistence, much as that failure is *evidence* for their nonexistence.

Thus, the upshot of Einstein's analysis concerning the issue before us is *not*, as Bridgman would have it, that the concepts of science refer to our operations instead of to the properties and relationships of physical events (7). What the restricted theory of relativity *does* teach us, however, is that the properties and relationships of physical events and things are different in several important respects from the ones that Newton had postulated. As Max Born has justly remarked in his recent paper "Physical reality" (8):

. . . the theory of relativity . . . has never abandoned all attempts to assign properties to matter, but has refined the method of doing so in order to conform with certain new experiences. . . . [The] root of the matter is a very simple logical distinction which seems to be obvious to anybody not biased by a solipsistic metaphysics; namely this: that often a measurable quantity is not a property of a thing, but a property of its relation to other things. . . . Most measurements in physics are not directly concerned with the things which interest us, but with some kind of projection, this word taken in the widest possible sense.

In particular, if natural clocks happen to be synchronized via light in the manner of Einstein's definition and if material rods are copresent with such clocks in the various Galilean frames, then these physical recording devices will show the readings required by the Lorentz transformations quite apart from any conscious human observer or "operator" (9), whereas Bridgman tells us (10) that

If the meanings of science are to be found in operations, then there must be a performer of the operations and this is of necessity a human performer.

In fact, as he himself recognizes, his meaning postulate coupled with the privacy of sense data, makes operationism fundamentally incompatible with the basic idea of relativity, which is the idea of *invariance* with respect to reference frames (*11*).

It should be noted that, although Bridgman does not deny the feasibility of a description of nature in terms of properties and relationships, he claims certain very definite advantages for a description based entirely on operations (*12*). What are these advantages and on what grounds does he claim them? He writes (*13*):

> What we are in effect doing in thus preferring the operational attack is to say what we *do* in meeting new physical situations has a greater stability than the situations themselves and that we can go further without revising our operations than we can without revising our picture of the properties of objects.

He attempts to illustrate this claim by specific reference to the history of relativity and says (*14*):

> Reflection on the situation after the event shows that it should not have needed the new experimental facts which led to relativity to convince us of the inadequacy of our previous concepts, but that a sufficiently shrewd analysis should have prepared us for at least the possibility of what Einstein did. . . . We should now make it our business to understand so thoroughly the character of our permanent mental relations to nature that another change in our attitude, such as that due to Einstein, shall be forever impossible.

And he adds that the only way of making sure that we can "render unnecessary the services of the unborn Einsteins" (*15*) is to refuse to link the same concept to a variety of operations, since this nonunique operational anchorage of concepts "subjects us to the constant danger that we may get different numbers by these different operations when experimental accuracy is improved" (*16*). I do not think that this thesis will bear examination.

Let us see whether careful attention to the operational anchorage of our concepts could have forestalled or lessened the surprises and revisions that were made necessary by relativity. Suppose that a unique operational procedure had been insisted on in classical physics for the specification of distances and that the same had been done for time determinations. Would that have forestalled the Newtonian assumptions of absolute simultaneity and of the nondependence of mass on velocity, thereby cushioning us against the surprising results of Kaufmann's experiments? To be sure, it would have done so in the sense that we would not have measured any group velocities exceeding that of light and we would then not have assumed the existence of signals of arbitrarily large velocities. Neither would we have felt that mass is always independent of velocity. But note the prohibitive price that would have had to be paid for this spurious gain: Newton's law of universal gravitation and third law of motion with their instantaneous action-at-a-distance could not have been enunciated. Neither could Newton have stated his second law of motion, for it tells us that a material particle can be brought to an arbitrarily large velocity by a sufficiently large force acting for a sufficiently long time, if the mass is assumed constant regardless of the velocity. In short, the price of the *safety* that could have been attained by operationist caution and restraint would have been, among other things, the immensely fruitful system of classical celestial mechanics! In fact, if the rule of operationist caution is strictly and consistently applied, physics must reduce to a mere record of isolated data, since the criterion does not warrant making extrapolations in *any* direction. In particular, how, in the absence of the information yielded by the experiments of the years between 1900 and 1905, could a *safe* yet *nonsterile* theory of mechanics have been constructed at all? And how could attention to unique operational anchorage of concepts have immunized classical optics against the results of the Michelson-Morley experiment without first rendering that theoretical discipline almost totally impotent? It is quite true that operational awareness would have made us less surprised to find that the length of a moving body is different from the corresponding rest length of that body and less prone to make the unconscious *a priori* assumption that these lengths are equal. But awareness of the inductive leaps involved in the postulational and extrapolative ascription of *properties* and *relationships* to physical things would have secured the safe advantages for us without sacrificing the immense theoretical fruitfulness achievable through a description in terms of properties. Thus, in the case of length, it is not attention to operations of measurement but Cantor's *theory,* formulated in terms of properties and relationships, that tells us that we cannot determine the length of a body AB on the basis of the number of points between A and B, because there are just as many points in a short segment as in a long one. When this result is coupled with the purely theoretically discovered Riemannian theory of manifolds, it becomes clear that the length of body AB cannot be an attribute of the space between the points A and B or a relationship between these points but must be an attribute of the relationship between the body AB on the one hand and the standard of congruence on the other.

An analogous consideration can be advanced against the operationist's invocation of the principle of equivalence of the *general* theory of relativity, since this principle lends itself to formulation both in terms of properties and in terms of theoretical operations. In all these cases, a description in terms of properties and relationships yields all the advantages secured by an operational description. But a description based on properties also secures for us a range of theoretical fruitfulness that no genuine operational description could ever hope to achieve. In fact, it is a description based on properties that explains, among other things, why it is that diverse operations do *or* do not yield the same numerical results under certain conditions and tells us how to enlarge our operational horizons through new experiments (*17*).

It seems inevitable, therefore, that the price of fruitfulness is a description in terms of properties and relationships that entails the risk of requiring the services of unborn Einsteins! This is not to deny that *historically,* a kind of operational critique contributed to the abandonment of H. A. Lorentz's form of the ether hypothesis, a hypothesis whose vacuity becomes equally apparent, however, upon asking what *properties* and *relationships* are intelligibly ascribed by that hypothesis to physical objects and events (*18*).

Thus, as I see it, operationism can contribute significantly to our knowledge, if it is construed as part of the restricted discipline of pragmatics but *not* if it is interpreted as an account of the logic or semantics of physics. And only the failure to distinguish between pragmatics and semantics can confer plausibility on Bridgman's view that the philosophical innovations of restricted relativity lend support to the

subjectivism of homocentric operationism or of phenomenalistic positivism.

NOTES

1. P. W. Bridgman, *The Logic of Modern Physics* (Macmillan,
   New York, 1927), pp. 1–9 [referred to later as *LMP*]; *The
   Nature of Physical Theory* (Princeton Univ. Press, Princeton,
   N. J., 1936), pp. 8–10 [referred to later as *NPT*]; "Some implications of recent points of view in physics," *Rev. Intern.
   Phil.* No. 10 (1949), pp. 1–3 [referred to later as *RPVP*]; "The
   operational aspect of meaning," *Synthèse* 8, 255 (1950–51)
   [referred to later as *OAM*]; "The Nature of some of our physical
   concepts," *Brit. J. Phil. Sci.* 1, 258 (1951); *Sci. Monthly* 79,
   32 (July 1954).
2. *OAM*, p. 253; see also *NPT*, pp. 8–9.
3. H. Reichenbach, *Philosophic Foundations of Quantum Mechanics* (Univ. of California Press, Berkeley, 1948); see also
   L. W. Beck, *Phil. Science* 17, 82–83 (1950) and H. Reichenbach, *The Direction of Time* (Univ. of California Press, Berkeley, 1956), p. 223.
4. *RPVP*, pp. 3–4; see also *OAM*, p. 256.
5. *RPVP*, pp. 11–18, and *NPT*, pp. 33–34.
6. H. Mehlberg, "Essai sur la théorie causale du temps," I, *Studia
   Philosophica* (1935), pp. 119–260; E. Zilsel, Über die Asym-
   metrie der Kausalität und die Einsinnigkeit der Zeit," *Natur-
   wissenschaften* 15, 282 (1927); K. G. Denbigh, "Thermodynamics and the subjective sense of time," *Brit. J. Phil. Sci.* 4,
   185 (1953); A. Grübaum, "Time and Entropy," *American
   Scientist* 43, 550 (1955) [a revised version of this paper is to
   appear in German in the *Archiv für Philosophie*]; A. Grünbaum, "Carnap's views on the foundations of geometry," in
   P. A. Schilpp, Ed., *The Philosophy of Rudolf Carnap*, Library
   of Living Philosophers, vol. X (Tudor, New York, in press);
   P. W. Bridgman, *Reflections of a Physicist* (Philosophical Library, New York, 1950), pp. 165–167; P. W. Bridgman, "Reflections on Thermodynamics," *American Scientist* 41, 549
   (1953).
7. See *OAM*, pp. 255–256; *NPT*, pp. 9–10; and *LMP*, pp. 6–9.
   For details on the material from the special theory of relativity
   which is pertinent here, see A. Grünbaum, "Logical and Philosophical Foundations of the Special Theory of Relativity,"
   American J. of Physics 23, 450 (1955), §2, and "Fundamental
   Philosophical Issues in the Special Theory of Relativity" in
   K. Sapper (ed.) *Kritik und Fortbildung der Relativitätstheorie*,
   to be published in Europe.
8. M. Born, *Phil. Quarterly* 3, 143 (1953).

9. H. Reichenbach, *Axiomatik der relativistischen Raum-Zeit-Lehre* (Vieweg, Braunschweig, 1924), p. 70.

10. *RPVP*, p. 18. This meaning postulate leads Bridgman to make a curious aprioristic pronouncement in regard to concepts that will prove fruitful in social theory, for he thinks that the postulate guarantees that "*The individual is the unit in terms of which all our social concepts ultimately find their meanings*" (*ibid.*, p. 20).

11. P. W. Bridgman, "Einstein's theories and the operational point of view," in P. A. Schilpp, Ed., *Albert Einstein: Philosopher-Scientist*, Library of Living Philosophers, vol. VII (Evanston, Ill., 1949), pp. 335–354, and Einstein's reply, *ibid.*, p. 679; *RPVP*, p. 19.

12. See *NPT*, pp. 9–10.

13. *OAM*, p. 257.

14. *LMP*, pp. 1–2.

15. *LMP*, p. 24.

16. *OAM*, p. 255. See also *RPVP*, p. 3, but note Einstein's own contrary attitude on p. 193 of his "Geometry and experience," as reprinted in Feigl and Brodbeck, Eds., *Readings in the Philosophy of Science* (Appleton-Century-Crofts, New York, 1953).

17. This point is illustrated with respect to the concept of pressure by R. B. Lindsay in "A critique of operationalism in physics," *Phil. Science* **4**, 458 (1937).

18. For a logical analysis of the supplantation of specific Lorentzian philosophical conceptions by Einstein, see A. Grünbaum, "Logical and Philosophical Foundations of the Special Theory of Relativity," *American J. of Physics* **23**, 450 (1955), §5.

Chapter 3

Freud's Psychoanalytic Theory

Confirmation of Psychoanalytic Theories

by Else Frenkel-Brunswik

FREUD'S IDEAS in the sphere of personality at first aroused a clamor of protest that has never entirely subsided. Once the initial shock ensuing from Freud's discoveries had been overcome, however, the scrutinies of the system appear to be concerned more with its formal or methodological characteristics than with its content. Thus we hear of the alleged subjectivism or animism of psychoanalysis, of its confusion of hypotheses and facts, or of the nonverifiability of its hypotheses.

Many of the objections against psychonanalysis have their origin in an overly narrow interpretation of scientific empiricism or of operationism, and generally in a vaguely antitheoretical attitude. Since it is the physical sciences that are usually taken as the ideal model of scientific theory construction and of operational procedure, certain fundamental changes in the conception of theoretical structure that have taken place in the field of physics itself must be taken into consideration. Philipp Frank (1) points out that the earlier ultrapositivistic requirements, according to which all principles of physics should be formulated by using only observable qualities, has been broadened to include indirection; Einstein (2) speaks of "the ever-widening logical gap" between observation and basic concepts or laws. According to Hempel (3), it is precisely the "fictitious concepts rather than those fully definable by observables" that enable science to proceed to explanation and prediction.

A comparison between the situation in physics and in psychoananlysis is certainly not in all respects justified. However, modern physics and psychoanalysis have in common a turning away from the "natural" to a "fictitious" lan-

NOTE: This is a condensation of the writer's monograph, *Psychoanalysis and the Unity of Science* [*Proc. Am. Acad. Arts Sci.* 80, No. 4 (1954)], which was sponsored by the Institute for the Unity of Science in Boston. Some of the views expressed herein were first formulated in 1940 (see ref. 10).

guage. And the common result of this policy is that a wider and simpler network of interrelationships within observable data is ultimately being achieved. The fact that theoretical constructs, such as "unconsciousness," "id," "superego," or "repression," refer only indirectly, and not completely at that, to observable data must therefore not be made the basis of an objection against psychoanalysis as such. It may be helpful in the early stages of discovery to designate certain patterns of behavior in terms of the special and relatively fixed classifications listed. Today many of the earlier statements of psychoanalysis may be reformulated in terms of behavioral patterns in such a manner that the facets of behavior connected with the more genuinely biological and instinctual processes—the id—are differentiated from those that are the result of cultural and parental commands and taboos—the superego.

Whereas in Europe the most important function of logical positivism was to stress the necessity of relating existing theories to empirical data, in this country, and especially in the case of the social sciences, its major function seems to be the advocacy of the formation of, and a tolerance for, theory per se.

With regard to the definition of basic concepts, some critics of psychoanalysis have objected to an alleged lack of sophistication in Freud concerning the philosophy of science and to his tendency to "reify" his concepts. Actually Freud, in contrast to some of his followers, was keenly aware of logical and epistemological problems. Definitions in science, he maintains (4, p. 60f),

. . . are in the nature of conventions; although everything depends on their being chosen in no arbitrary manner, but determined by the important relations they have to the empirical material—relations that we seem to divine before we can clearly recognize and demonstrate them. . . . Progressively we must modify these concepts so that they become widely applicable and at the same time consistent logically. Then, indeed, it may be time to immure them in definitions. . . . The science of physics furnishes an excellent illustration of the way in which even those "basic concepts" that are firmly established in the form of definitions are constantly being altered in their content.

Most clinical descriptions found in Ferud employ the inferential construct of the "unconscious." Freud considers the assumption of unconsciousness as necessary because the data of consciousness are "exceedingly defective" (5, p. 22). Conscious acts alone do not enable us to account for certain aspects of slips of tongue and of other parapraxes, of dreams, of mental symptoms or obsessions in the sick, let alone the sudden inspirations of healthy persons. In carrying us, as Freud says, "beyond the limitations of direct experience," the assumption of unconscious acts makes the disconnected and unintelligible conscious acts fall into a demonstrable connection.

From the standpoint of the logic of science, unconscious tendencies are a special case of latent or "dispositional" characteristics. They are comparable to such physical characteristics as magnetism, provided that we do not insist on assigning them to "the mind" in a metaphysical sense. Such composite terms as "unconscious hostility" or "dependency" describe a disposition to display aggression or dependence under specified conditions, for example, in therapy. In his definition of behavior Carnap (6) has expressly included "dispositions to behavior which may not be manifest in a given special case." We therefore must agree with Freud that it is the very assumption of unconscious processes that enables psychoanalysis to take its place as "a natural science like any other" (7). He goes on to explain that these processes are "in themselves just as unknowable as those dealt with by other sciences such as physics and chemistry." And he remains in the spirit of the natural sciences when he stresses that "it is possible to establish the laws which those processes obey and to follow over long and unbroken stretches their mutual relation and interdependences" (p. 36).

Originally the concepts of conscious and unconscious signify particular "systems" possessed of certain dynamic characteristics, calling for a specification of their relationships within the over-all formal model. When dreams or subsequent free associations are used, this is done for the establishment of intermediate links that can be inserted in the gap between the two systems and that help to recover the latent material in a process of interpretation. Obviously to avoid confusion concerning mentalistic reification, Freud suggests "employing for the recognized mental systems certain arbitrarily chosen names." But since he cannot ignore consciousness as the common point of departure, he proposes to use the abbreviation Cs (for consciousness) and Ucs (for the unconscious) when the two words are used in the systematic sense.

Only in Freud's later writings does the term "unconscious" take on a distinct reference to mental qualities. One of the chief reasons for this shift was the empirical realization that not only the id but also the superego is in part unconscious. In effect this merely underscores the increasing emphasis on the system-character of Freud's basic concepts and the decreasing emphasis on the more introspectionistic distinction between conscious and unconscious.

Freud readily acknowledges that a "rough correlation of . . . the mental apparatus to anatomy . . . exists." If so far every attempt to establish a localization of his constructs has miscarried, the present imperfect state of the biological sciences must be held responsible. Siegfried Bernfeld (8) has amply pointed out the influence of Helmholtz' physicalism and of the principle of conservation of energy on Freud. But it must be stressed that while at the beginning Freud was intensely dominated by neuro-physiological thinking, the decisive progress in psychoanalysis did not occur until after he freed himself from the search for such analogies and turned to more openly psychological models.

In defending the complexities of his approach, Freud stresses that there is no obligation to achieve at our very first attempt a theory that "commends itself by its simplicity, in which all is plain sailing." Freud argues that we must defend complexities of the theory itself so long as we find that they fit in with the results of observation; yet we must not abandon our expectation of being guided in the end by those very complexities to the recognition of "a state of affairs that is at once simple in itself and at the same time answers to all the complications of reality" (9, p. 122). If we note a similarity of tone with logical empiricism, we must not forget the fascination that in turn psychoanalysis has had for many of the logical empiricists; they have seen the genius of Freud at a time when most psychologists and psychiatrists were still deeply resistant.

Next to the concept of the unconscious, it is that of "instinct" which has been objected to most vigorously in the face of claims of psychoanalysis for consideration as a science. The psychoanalytic concept of instinct is complicated by the assumption of far-reaching transformations and disguises, particularly of the sex instinct. In reality, some parts of Freud's instinct theory, notably the theory of infantile sexuality and of the psychosexual stages of development, belong to the most lucid and most powerfully executed portions of the psychoanalytic system. As in the case of the unconscious, Freud pursues an essentially operational course in defining the instincts. He does so in pointing to the capacity of the instincts to "act vicariously for one another" and to readily change their objects. The mechanisms of repression, of reversal into the opposite, or of sublimation are some of the more striking examples of this variability. It may well be argued that the explanatory value of the concept of instinct lies precisely in this emphasis on variability. Only in the case of an assumed one-to-one correspondence between instinct and manifest behavior would the concept of instinct become circular or superfluous as an unnecessary duplication of behavior. Freud's concept of instinct is a truly explanatory, inferential construct imbued with some degree of independence. He avoided unnecessary duplication by fully considering the functional ambiguities inherent in the relationships between drives and behavior rather than by directly projecting behavioral trends back into the subjects.

The mixture of pioneering gusto with an understanding for ultimate logical requirements, which is so characteristic of Freud, is revealed when he speaks of the "superb indefiniteness" of the concept of instinct. He goes on to claim for the instincts "the same value as approximations as belongs to the corresponding intellectual scaffolding found in other natural sciences." We must expect them to "remain for a considerable time no less indeterminate than those of the sciences (force, mass, attraction, etc.)" (7, p. 36).

Freud ascribes some of the difficulties in his speculations about the instincts—speculations that he likes to call his "mythology"—to our being obligated to operate with "metaphorical expressions peculiar to psychology." We must add in his behalf that, for the type of problems with which psychoanalysis deals, the mentalistic—introspectionist or animistic—vocabulary constitutes the precise counterpart to what Frank (1) calls the "pictural" vocabulary, and that in turn this latter vocabulary is recognized in physics as a legitimate or at least tolerable ingredient of the earlier stages of concept formation. Whereas the analogical procedure may not be suited for purposes of ultimately proving a scientific hypothesis, it may well be argued that the function of mentalistic analogies is more important in psychology than it is in physics.

One of the most bewildering aspects of psychoanalytic theory is the turning away from the obvious face-value picture of personality as it derives from introspection or from the direct, "phenotypical" observation of external behavior segments. An example is the reinterpretation of overt friendliness as a sign of underlying hostility, or of extreme tidiness as a sign of preoccupation with dirt. The discrepancy disappears with the specification of a set of fixed or variable operational conditions that determine when overt behavior is to be interpreted as "genuine" and when as manifesting some heterogeneous latent factor.

Since scientific inference concerning "central" processes —that is, the assumption of internal states on the basis of external evidence—cannot be defended unless it is based on a wide variety of circumstantial evidence (10), central inference can be said not to have been legitimately attempted before psychoanalysis. It can be shown that on the negative side of the ledger psychoanalysis, especially in its beginnings, has comparatively de-emphasized both the surface manifestations in their specific identity and—what is more—the so-called "distal" achievements of behavior. These latter results of behavior in turn play the dominant role in Darwin's thinking and in such neo-behaviorist systems as that of Tolman (11). The regrouping of manifest observable facts as undertaken by Freud centers about sameness of "need"—that is, sameness of assumed internal cause or dynamism—while in the case of Tolman it centers about sameness of effect and, as we may add, in the case of Egon Brunswik's theory of perceptual thing-constancy (12) it centers about sameness of external object.

By virtue of this inherent incompleteness, psychoanalysis did not altogether manage to avoid the pitfalls of motivational relativism and of a genetic dissolution of overt adjustmental values. This one-sidedness has, to a certain extent, been remedied in the more recent turning of psychoanalysis from an almost exclusive emphasis on the id and on motivation to an increased concern with the ego—that is, with reality-oriented behavior and with adjustment in general. Even so, psychoanalytic expansion in this direction has been more programmatic than real, and there are a number of problems that can be solved only by an explicit integration of psychoanalysis with psychology proper and with sociology. The conceptual tools of psychoanalysis just are not sufficient to explain fully rational and social behavior (10). In fact, if we were to deny this we would obscure the essential theoretical contribution of Freud, which is his discovery of motivational dynamics.

In the context of adjustment problems, Freud tends to view character structure from a merely "defensive" point of view—that is, in terms of protecting oneself from internal threats rather than in terms of external task orientation—and social influences are seen as a series of traumata that bring to a halt or discontinue instinctual gratification and expression. While providing an understanding of an important aspect of the individual's attitude toward society, this view does not do justice to all the satisfactions gained from moving along constructive social avenues.

With all this said it must be granted that so far as motivation, per se, is concerned, psychoanalysis has achieved a legitimate reconstruction of objective causes rather than a mere pseudo-explanation in terms of subjectively experienced motives as such critics as Toulmin (13) and Flew (14) would have it. Far from identifying the introspectively reported motive and the objective explanation, the major merit of psychoanalysis is to have differentiated the two and unmasked and "discredited" as to their explanatory value the subjective experiences of motivation. The phenotypical, "manifest" characteristics are taken to provide only the indirect cues for inferences concerning the "latent," genotypical forces of motivation. It is of comparatively lesser significance that in the majority of cases it is verbal behavior such as dreams, free associations, and the like, rather than overt motor behavior proper, that psychoanalysis takes as the manifest basis for drive interpretations. This does not mean, however, that psychoanalysis is "introspectionistic." As everyone knows, it is precisely through psychoanalysis that we have learned to doubt the face value of introspection.

It must further be pointed out that the assumption of the dynamisms of the "inner man" to which such behaviorist critics of psychoanalysis as Skinner (15) have objected can be shown to increase the parsimony of the scientific description of behavior patterns. A translation of the psychoanalytic concepts into the terminology of the classical behaviorist's so-called "stimulus-response" approach, useful as it may be in certain contexts, has its difficulties and limitations. As we have seen, the major emphasis of psychoanalysis is on the discovery of internal causes; these include, in the language of psychoanalysis, "subjective phantasies" and generally the differential meanings an external event may acquire for various individuals. Freud began to make progress in his understanding of hysteria only after he had given up the idea of a simple external causation. Freud points out that only after the hypothetical factor of the hysterical phantasies had been introduced did the structure of the neurosis and its relationship to the patient "become conspicuous." Since the relationship of these phantasies to external factors is most complex and ambiguous, it seems heuristically fruitful to assume the internal mechanisms postulated by psychoanalysis, leaving their full operational specification for a later time. Contrary to Skinner, I believe that such assumptions do not carry us outside the "bounds of natural science." But I do agree with Skinner on the point that any "looking inside the organism for an explanation of behavior" can easily lead to a neglect of some of the environmental factors and readily acknowledge that it has done so in the case of psychoanalysis.

Even more crucial is the fact that hypothetical extrapolations from overt behavior help to select the most relevant, though often less conspicuous, aspects of behavior which otherwise would be lost in the practically infinite range of possible observation. The relatively great explanatory and predictive value of hypotheses dealing with underlying motivation can be demonstrated statistically by means of multiple correlation (16). It is without doubt based on the fact that the selectivity just referred to enters crucially into the formation of these hypotheses. We may add that, from the standpoint of logical analysis, there is no alternative but to be behavioristic in any psychological endeavor; neither the so-called "subjective phantasies" in which psychoanalysis is interested, nor "introspective" events of any kind in others, can be constituted except by inference from the manifest physical observation of organisms.

In the process of theory-construction, Freud is generally

quite careful in attempting to distinguish what we now call the "postulatory" from what we now call the "operational" elements of the theory, at the same time allowing their interplay as he moves along. However, his system would benefit from greater formalization and especially also from a more systematic differentiation between basic assumptions and their derivations. For example, a combination of the assumptions of infantile sexuality and of repression may be able to cover many of the more specific theorems in psychoanalysis.

Feigl (17) places psychoanalysis at the third of the four "levels" of explanation he distinguishes, thus grouping it together with the relatively descriptive behavior theories of Tolman and Hull. To me it seems that at least a certain group of psychoanalytic concepts, including that of the unconscious, goes beyond this level by involving what Reichenbach (18) calls "surplus meaning." In terms of a distinction recently injected into psychological theory by MacCorquodale and Meehl (19), this latter group of concepts would seem to be "hypothetical constructs," in contradistinction to the "intervening variables" which are thought of as resting exclusively on the values of a specified set of empirically observed data. In their own rather sketchy analysis, the last-named authors point out that such terms as "libido," "censorship," or "superego" were in psychoanalysis originally introduced as intervening variables—that is, as conventionalized designations of observable properties—but that there frequently was an unnoticed shift toward hypothetical constructs.

In their arguments the authors tend to overlook the fact that statements containing intervening variables are by no means exhaustible by statements concerning their observational basis. Both Carnap (6) and Hempel (3) have made it clear that sentences containing disposition terms cannot be fully translated into sentences about observables. Since we cannot specify all conditions and manners in which latent tendencies become manifest, dispositional statements involve "open" terms and require an infinite series of conditions in order to be tested.

The distinction between intervening variables and hypothetical constructs may, in my opinion, nonetheless be retained as a gradual one involving different degrees of indirectness of evidence or different kinds of surplus meaning.

Possible relationships to the distinction made by Carnap and Hempel between postulatory theoretical constructs and concepts more directly reducible to observation could be pointed out. Guided by some relatively fragmentary initial empirical observations, Freud seems to have proceeded rather directly to the building of a hypothetical theoretical structure, with empirical interpretation lagging somewhat behind; in the definition of such theoretical constructs as superego, ego, and id, the major emphasis is on their structural relationships to one another rather than on their relationships to observation. His frequent oscillation between hypothetical constructs and intervening variables has afforded some protection against both a too narrow operationalism and the dangers of meaningless generalization.

Considering now briefly the attempts at confirmation of psychoanalytic hypotheses, it must be pointed out that by involving concepts more removed from the immediate data, psychoanalysis has lengthened the chains of intellectual and experimental work that connect the principles with the observational protocols. We may recall here the statement of Frank (1) that modern physics requires special ingenuity in verifying its theories and that this fact is a result of the greater abstractness of concepts. Traditional Newtonian physics could easily be verified by observation, since it was a direct formulation of everyday experience, obvious and plausible to common sense, whereas in Einstein's general theory of relativity "the description of the operations by which the quantities involved could be measured becomes a serious and complex task. It becomes an essential part of the theory" (1, p. 19f).

Psychoanalysis shares with modern physics the fact that its statements do not lend themselves to the most direct and obvious types of confirmation. In each case, the highly interpretive statements involved do not carry the rules of their confirmation as obviously with themselves as do more descriptive statements. In reviewing the extensive literature on objective studies of psychoanalytic hypotheses (20, 21), one is impressed by the fact that the more descriptive types of hypotheses involved in the theory of "fixation" and "regression" proved to be more readily accessible to experimental confirmation than the more explanatory ones on "repression," "projection," and "reaction formation." This may indeed be due to the fact that the latter derive from the more inferential and abstract parts of psychoanalytic theory. Complex conditions, such as those involved in the analysis of transference, are required before that which has been repressed may become conscious. Misunderstandings of psychoanalytic theory have arisen when statements concerning repression that originally were intended to refer to unconscious—that is, inferred rather than overt—processes, were erroneously taken as purely descriptive statements of conscious contents. As in physics, a simple identification of statements containing disposition terms with statements about manifest events is not permissible. Still and all, some of the experimental studies have verified even such seemingly far-fetched psychoanalytic assumptions as symbolism.

A type of approach other than the experimental, and one that I have tried to develop for a number of years, concentrates on the principle of alternative manifestations of motivational tendencies. This principle describes the basic pattern of interrelationships between the two strata involved in all psychoanalytic theory, the manifest and the latent, and can be shown to underlie most if not all of the specific mechanisms just mentioned. The possibility of analyzing statistically the tangled relationships between the two strata after imbuing them with some degree of operational independence may be illustrated by a study dealing with motivation in its relation to overt behavior segments (16) and one dealing with certain mechanisms of self-deception (22). In the former study a comparison of over-all motivational ratings with specific behavioral manifestations is used for a "rational reconstruction" of the cues underlying the so-called "intuitive inferences" made by the clinicians; the same general procedure would apply in case of the more explicit and more scrutinizing inferences concerning motivational dynamics made by the psychologist as a scientist rather than as a synoptic rater. Knowledge of the type of drive variable involved seems to hold good promise for behavior prediction of an "either-or" type, further specification of which must hinge on other than "dynamic" factors. Among these further factors determining, whether, say, underlying aggression is worked out in a socially constructive form or in neurotic symptoms, such situational factors as social and economic or occupational conditions must be assigned a major role.

In our study of self-deception, certain formal criteria of distortion, which may take their place alongside the more content-oriented type of diagnostic criteria favored in psychoanalysis proper, were established by means of a linguistic analysis of the individuals' responses. For example, favorable self-descriptions that do not correspond to the manifest behavioral realities are frequently formulated in exaggerated terms. The use of such linguistic or semantic devices as superlatives, generalizations, and repetitions was found to be statistically concomitant with a shortcoming rather than a strength in the area concerned.

In the verification of psychoanalytic hypotheses, the systematic evidence furnished by academic psychology constitutes only one of several avenues. Psychoanalysis itself has provided confirmatory, though seldom rigorous, empirical evidence of overwhelming scope, ranging from the wealth of material accumulated from individual patients to a synopsis of dream mechanisms, of lapses of tongue and memory, of pathologic symptoms, and of certain relevant features of folklore, myth, and other cultural phenomena. Regardless of how imperfect psychoanalytic theory may be in its formal structure, it has no rival among psychological theories as far as the range of both its evidence and its explanatory power is concerned.

Some of the obstacles encountered in the efforts to separate manifest behavior and latent motivation, or surface and depth in general, go beyond the merely methodological difficulties encountered in the process of scientific verification. One of these additional difficulties is a semantic one. The vocabulary of everyday language does not furnish us consistently with two separate sets of terms, one for overt behavior and the other for underlying motivation. Unless we drastically depart from familiar usage, the term "friendliness," for example, stands either for the basically friendly outlook on life or for the techniques of friendliness—genuine or fake—by which this basic outlook may be implemented or pretended, or for both. This dilemma is in a formal sense similar to the one presented by the two-faced meaning of our common perceptual terms (12). These terms also tend to have double reference, one to the personal and somewhat variable perceptual response, and the other to the interpersonal, measured physical stimulus. Most perceptual qualities exhibit highly tangled relationships to a variety of measured stimulus variables. The conceptual separation of perceptual stimulus and perceptual response can thus no longer appear as a case of entities superfluously multiplied; neither can, we may add, the separation of "behavior" and "motivation" with their similarly tangled relationships, as outlined in some of the foregoing paragraphs.

Certainly, both the motivations and the behaviors are constituted from overt behavior, as both stimuli and perceptual responses are constituted from different types of observational experiences. But motivations are arrived at through a synopsis of the constant elements in many bits of behavior. The problem of the genuineness of behavior that I have pointed out as crucial in the context of proving psychoanalytic hypotheses illustrates the need that the two sets of events be made conceptually and operationally independent of each other so that their far-reaching actual independence under the principle of alternative manifestations can be brought out. An independent nomenclature for the different levels will thus in the end have to be established. This would remove much of the temptation to fall back into an oversimplified, prepsychoanalytic, single-level or surface treatment of the motivational aspects of behavior.

It has been observed that each time separations of the kind just described had to be substituted for previous identifications in the history of science, there was irrational, emotional resistance against the recognition of the equivocations or ambiguities involved. Besides their applicability to our outlook on psychoanalysis in particular, these resistances have some bearing on the topic of one of the other symposiums of this conference, the acceptance or rejection of scientific theories in general. They may also be linked with what I have called "intolerance of ambiguity" (23). Acceptance of the ambiguous relationship between motivation and manifestation, which is the chief discovery of psychoanalysis, requires cognitive tolerance of ambiguity on the part of the scientist. Its opposite, the concretistic, compulsive, and dogmatic patterns of perception and thought that have been so vividly described by both psychiatrists and psychoanalysts and are not infrequent among scientists are not conducive to the acceptance of psychoanalysis.

A final word must be added concerning the true or alleged ethical implications of psychoanalysis. Together with the cognitive resistances just outlined, ethical connotations may be the chief determinants of the acceptance and further destiny of any scientific theory. It has been objected against psychoanalysis—perhaps more often in the past than in the present—that its orientation is fundamentally amoral. Arguments of this kind were raised, not only by philosophers in search of a system of absolute values, but also by empirically oriented social scientists and psychologists of major stature, among them Max Weber (24). Weber saw in psychoanalysis an expression of a tendency to loosen our basic ethical principles. In a letter of 1907 Weber had accused Freud of proposing a psychiatric or "nerves" ethics characterized by the prevalence of the "hygienic" point of view (25, p. 417).

Against these strictures it may be said that, with all the reservations that psychoanalysis has voiced against an overly naive rational interpretation of ethics, it has merely turned against the assumed major executive principle of the traditional forms of ethics rather than against their basic constructive content. This particular executive principle is the mechanism of repression. Most pre-psychoanalytic ethical systems stress such inhibitory devices as the looking away from evil, or its denial, or its mastery through strength of will. From psychoanalysis we have learned about the inefficiency and the dangers of these various forms of repression; from the same source we have learned of the importance of consciousness, integration, and maturity. All that is considered an essential ingredient of maturity in psychoanalysis, such as rationality, the overcoming of aggression, cooperativeness, the ability to love and to work, and the courage to face inside and outside threats that oppose these characteristics, bespeak standards that stand up well among the traditional systems of ethics. In psychoanalysis every neurosis is in and by itself considered as failure at moral control. The important historical contribution of traditional systems of ethics is the attempt to strengthen consciousness and conscience against the invasion of the instincts; through psychoanalysis we have become aware that such strengthening can be achieved only by facing and working through, rather than by merely condemning, the forces threatening our conscious personal and social values. From this latter viewpoint the mortal sin is self-deception and lack of insight rather than a lack of repression.

It may be that the diversion of attention from the functions of reason in psychoanalysis has contributed to the semblance of ethical relativism. As we have seen, psychoanalysis was so overwhelmed by its epoch-making discovery of the role of irrational forces that the explicit exploration of reasoning processes was temporarily obscured, even though it was reason and not the irrational that held the top spot so far as the evaluative attitude of psychoanalysis is concerned.

There is an illuminating reversal in the role played by reason when we compare the direct verbal formulations made by Freud, on the one hand, and Weber or Durkheim (26), on the other, with the actual function of reason in the theoretical edifices of these men. Both Durkheim and Weber have repeatedly been described as rationalists, albeit both see the foundations of society in fundamentally non-rational moral qualities. Freud, on the other hand, has been criticized for having given too much prominence to the irrational, while in fact his one hope is the overcoming of the irrational in a society built on reason. Freud neglected to explore reason directly and challenged the potency of reason in guiding human conduct. But in his evaluations of the goals of human development he has an exalted esteem for reason, and his understanding for the vicissitudes of unreason has sharpened his grasp for the fundamental nature of reason; in this more crucial respect he is a believer in reason in the best sense of the word.

NOTES

1. P. Frank, *Modern Science and Its Philosophy* (Harvard Univ. Press, Cambridge, Mass., 1941).

2. A. Einstein, in *The Philosophy of Bertrand Russell*, Library of Living Philosophers, vol. 5, P. A. Schilpp, Ed. (Northwestern Univ. Press, Evanston, Ill., 1944), p. 289.

3. C. G. Hempel, *Fundamentals of concept formation in empirical science*, in *Intern. Encycl. Unified Sci.* vol. II, No. 7 (Univ. of Chicago Press, Chicago, 1952).

4. S. Freud, "Instincts and their vicissitudes" (1915), *Collected Papers* (Hogarth, London, 1925), vol. 4, pp. 60–83.

5. ———, "A note on the unconscious in psychoanalysis" (1912), *Collected Papers*, vol. 4, pp. 22–29.

6. R. Carnap, *Phil. Sci.* 3, 420 (1936); 4, 2 (1937).

7. S. Freud, *An Outline of Psychoanalysis* (1940), J. Strachey, Tr. (Norton, New York, 1949).

8. S. Bernfeld, *Psychoanal. Quart,* 13, 341 (1944).

9. S. Freud, "The unconscious" (1915), *Collected Papers*, vol. 4, 98–136.
10. E. Frenkel-Brunswik, *J. Abnormal & Social Psychol.* 35, 176 (1940).
11. E. C. Tolman, *Purposive Behavior in Animals and Men* (Century, New York, 1932).
12. E. Brunswik, *Wahrnehmung und Gegenstandswelt* (Deuticke, Vienna, 1934).
13. S. Toulmin, *Analysis* 9, 23 (1948).
14. A. Flew, *ibid.* 10, 8 (1949).
15. B. F. Skinner, *Science and Human Behavior* (Macmillan, New York, 1953).
16. E. Frenkel-Brunswik, *Motivation and Behavior* (Genetic Psychol. Monogr., 1942).
17. H. Feigl, in *Readings in Philosophical Analysis,* H. Feigl and W. Sellars, Eds. (Appleton-Century-Crofts, New York, 1949).
18. H. Reichenbach, *Experience and Prediction* (Univ. of Chicago Press, Chicago, 1938).
19. K. MacCorquodale and P. Meehl, *Psychol. Rev.* 55, 95 (1948).
20. E. R. Hilgard, in *Psychoanalysis as Science,* E. Pumpian-Mindlin, Ed. (Stanford Univ. Press, Calif., 1952).
21. R. R. Sears, *Survey of Objective Studies of Psychoanalytic Concepts* (Social Sci. Research Council Monogr. No. 51, 1943).
22. E. Frenkel-Brunswik, *J. Social Psychol.* 10, 409 (1939).
23. ———, *J. Personality* 18, 108 (1949).
24. Max Weber, *The Protestant Ethic and the Spirit of Capitalism* (Scribner's, New York, 1930).
25. Marianne Weber, *Max Weber: Ein Lebensbild* (Lambert-Schneider, Heidelberg, 1950).
26. E. Durkheim, *The Rules of Sociological Method* (Free Press, Glencoe, Ill., 1950).

Critique of Psychoanalytic Concepts and Theories

by B. F. Skinner

FREUD'S GREAT CONTRIBUTION to Western thought has been described as the application of the principle of cause and effect to human behavior. Freud demonstrated that many features of behavior hitherto unexplained—and often dismissed as hopelessly complex or obscure—could be shown to be the product of circumstances in the history of the individual. Many of the causal relationships he so convincingly demonstrated had been wholly unsuspected—unsuspected, in particular, by the very individuals whose behavior they controlled. Freud greatly reduced the sphere of accident and caprice in our considerations of human conduct. His achievement in this respect appears all the more impressive when we recall that he was never able to appeal to the quantitative proofs characteristic of other sciences. He carried the day with sheer persuasion—with the massing of instances and the delineation of surprising parallels and analogies among seemingly diverse materials.

This was not, however, Freud's own view of the matter. At the age of seventy he summed up his achievement in this way (1):

> My life has been aimed at one goal only: to infer or guess how the mental apparatus is constructed and what forces interplay and counteract in it.

It is difficult to describe the mental apparatus he refers to in noncontroversial terms, partly because Freud's conception changed from time to time and partly because its very nature encouraged misinterpretation and misunderstanding. But it is perhaps not too wide of the mark to indicate its principal features as follows: Freud conceived of some realm of the mind, not necessarily having physical extent, but nevertheless capable of topographic description and of subdivision into regions of the conscious, coconscious, and unconscious. Within this space, various mental events —ideas, wishes, memories, emotions, instinctive tendencies, and so on—interacted and combined in many complex ways. Systems of these mental events came to be conceived of almost as subsidiary personalities and were given proper names: the id, the ego, and the superego. These systems divided among themselves a limited store of psychic energy. There were, of course, many other details.

No matter what logicians may eventually make of this mental apparatus, there is little doubt that Freud accepted it as real rather than as a scientific construct or theory. One does not at the age of seventy define the goal of one's life as the exploration of an explanatory fiction. Freud did not use his "mental apparatus" as a postulate system from which he deduced theorems to be submitted to empirical check. If there was any interaction between the mental apparatus and empirical observations, it took the form of modifying the apparatus to account for newly discovered facts. To many followers of Freud the mental apparatus appears to be equally as real, and the exploration of such an apparatus is similarly accepted as the goal of a science of behavior. There is an alternative view, however, which holds that Freud did not discover the mental apparatus but rather invented it, borrowing part of its structure from a traditional philosophy of human conduct but adding many novel features of his own devising.

There are those who will concede that Freud's mental apparatus was a scientific construct rather than an observable empirical system but who, nevertheless, attempt to justify it in the light of scientific method. One may take the line that metaphorical devices are inevitable in the early stages of any science and that although we may look with amusement today upon the "essences," "forces," "phlogistons," and "ethers" of the science of yesterday, these nevertheless were essential to the historical process. It would be difficult to prove or disprove this. However, if we have learned anything about the nature of scientific thinking, if mathematical and logical researches have improved our capacity to represent and analyze empirical data, it is possible that we can avoid some of the mistakes of adolescence. Whether Freud could have done so is past demonstrating, but whether we need similar constructs in the future prosecution of a science of behavior is a question worth considering.

Constructs are convenient and perhaps even necessary in dealing with certain complicated subject matters. As Frenkel-Brunswik shows (2), Freud was aware of the problems of scientific methodology and even of the metaphorical nature of some of his own constructs. When this was the case, he justified the constructs as necessary or at least highly convenient. But awareness of the nature of the metaphor is no defense of it, and if modern science is still occasionally metaphorical, we must remember that theory-wise it is also still in trouble. The point is not that metaphor or construct is objectionable but that particular metaphors and constructs have caused trouble and are continuing to do so. Freud recognized the damage worked by his own metaphorical thinking, but he felt that it could not be avoided and that the damage must be put up with. There is reason to disagree with him on this point.

Freud's explanatory scheme followed a traditional pattern of looking for a cause of human behavior inside the organism. His medical training supplied him with powerful supporting analogies. The parallel between the excision of a tumor, for example, and the release of a repressed wish from the unconscious is quite compelling and must have affected Freud's thinking. Now, the pattern of an inner explanation of behavior is best exemplified by doctrines of animism, which are primarily concerned with explaining the spontaneity and evident capriciousness of behavior. The living organism is an extremely complicated system behaving in an extremely complicated way. Much of its behavior appears at first blush to be absolutely unpredictable. The traditional procedure had been to invent an inner determiner, a "demon," "spirit," "homunculus," or "personality" capable of spontaneous change of course or of origination of action. Such an inner determiner offers only a momentary explanation of the behavior of the outer organism, because it must, of course, be accounted for also, but it is commonly used to put the matter beyond further inquiry and to bring the study of a causal series of events to a dead end.

Freud, himself, however, did not appeal to the inner apparatus to account for spontaneity or caprice because he was a thorough-going determinist. He accepted the responsibility of explaining, in turn, the behavior of the inner determiner. He did this by pointing to hitherto unnoticed external causes in the environmental and genetic history of the individual. He did not, therefore, need the traditional explanatory system for traditional purposes; but he was unable to eliminate the pattern from his thinking. It led him to represent each of the causal relationships he had discovered as a series of three events. Some environmental condition, very often in the early life of the individual, leaves an effect upon the inner mental apparatus, and this in turn produces the behavioral manifestation or symptom. Environmental event, mental state or process, behavioral symptom—these are the three links in Freud's causal chain. He made no appeal to the middle link to explain spontaneity or caprice. Instead he used it to bridge the gap in space and time between the events he had proved to be causally related.

A possible alternative, which would have had no quarrel

with established science, would have been to argue that the environmental variables leave *physiological* effects that may be inferred from the behavior of the individual, perhaps at a much later date. In one sense, too little is known at the moment of these physiological processes to make them useful in a legitimate way for this purpose. On the other hand, too much is known of them, at least in a negative way. Enough is known of the nervous system to place certain dimensional limits upon speculation and to clip the wings of explanatory fiction. Freud accepted, therefore, the traditional fiction of a mental life, avoiding an out-and-out dualism by arguing that eventually physiological counterparts would be discovered. Quite apart from the question of the existence of mental events, let us observe the damage that resulted from this maneuver.

We may touch only briefly upon two classical problems that arise once the conception of a mental life has been adopted. The first of these is to explain how such a life is to be observed. The introspective psychologists had already tried to solve this problem by arguing that introspection is only a special case of the observation upon which all science rests and that man's experience necessarily stands between him and the physical world with which science purports to deal. But it was Freud himself who pointed out that not all of one's mental life was accessible to direct observation—that many events in the mental apparatus were necessarily inferred. Great as this discovery was, it would have been still greater if Freud had taken the next step, advocated a little later by the American movement called Behaviorism, and insisted that conscious, as well as unconscious, events were inferences from the facts. By arguing that the individual organism simply reacts to its environment, rather than to some inner experience of that environment, the bifurcation of nature into physical and psychic can be avoided (3).

A second classical problem is how the mental life can be manipulated. In the process of therapy, the analyst necessarily acts upon the patient only through physical means. He manipulates variables occupying a position in the first link of Freud's causal chain. Nevertheless, it is commonly assumed that the mental apparatus is being directly manipulated. Sometimes it is argued that processes are initiated within the individual himself, such as those of free association and transference, and that these in turn act directly upon the mental apparatus. But how are these mental processes initiated by physical means? The clarification of such a causal connection places a heavy and often unwelcome burden of proof upon the shoulders of the dualist.

The important disadvantages of Freud's conception of mental life can be described somewhat more specifically. The first of these concerns the environmental variables to which Freud so convincingly pointed. The cogency of these variables was frequently missed because the variables were transformed and obscured in the course of being represented in mental life. The physical world of the organism was converted into conscious and unconscious experience, and these experiences were further transmuted as they combined and changed in mental processes. For example, early punishment of sexual behavior is an observable fact that undoubtedly leaves behind a changed organism. But when this change is represented as a state of conscious or unconscious anxiety or guilt, specific details of the punishment are lost. When, in turn, some unusual characteristic of the sexual behavior of the adult individual is related to the supposed guilt, many specific features of the relationship may be missed that would have been obvious if the same features of behavior had been related to the punishing episode. Insofar as the mental life of the individual is used as Freud used it to represent and to carry an environmental history, it is inadequate and misleading.

Freud's theory of the mental apparatus had an equally damaging effect upon his study of behavior as a dependent variable. Inevitably, it stole the show. Little attention was left to behavior per se. Behavior was relegated to the position of a mere mode of expression of the activities of the mental apparatus or the symptoms of an underlying disturbance. Among the problems not specifically treated in the manner that was their due, we may note five.

1) The nature of the act as a unit of behavior was never clarified. The simple *occurrence* of behavior was never well represented. "Thoughts" could "occur" to an individual; he could "have" ideas according to the traditional model; but he could "have" behavior only in giving expression to these inner events. We are much more likely to say that "the thought occurred to me to ask him his name" than that "the act of asking him his name occurred to me." It is in the na-

ture of thoughts and ideas that they occur to people, but we have never come to be at home in describing the emission of behavior in a comparable way. This is especially true of verbal behavior. In spite of Freud's valuable analysis of verbal slips and of the techniques of wit, and verbal art, he rejected the possibility of an analysis of verbal behavior in its own right rather than as the expression of ideas, feelings, or other inner events, and therefore missed the importance of this field for the analysis of units of behavior and the conditions of their occurrence.

The behavioral nature of perception was also slighted. To see an object as an object is not mere passive sensing; it is an act, and something very much like it occurs when we see an object although no object is present. Fantasy and dreams were for Freud not the perceptual *behavior* of the individual but pictures painted by an inner artist in some atelier of the mind which the individual then contemplated and perhaps then reported. This division of labor is not essential when the behavioral component of the act of seeing is emphasized.

2) The dimensions of behavior, particularly its dynamic properties, were never adequately represented. We are all familiar with the fact that some of our acts are more likely to occur upon a given occasion than others. But this likelihood is hard to represent and harder to evaluate. The dynamic changes in behavior that are the first concern of the psychoanalyst are primarily changes in probability of action. But Freud chose to deal with this aspect of behavior in other terms—as a question of "libido," "cathexis," "volume of excitation," "instinctive or emotional tendencies," "available quantities of psychic energy," and so on. The delicate question of how probability of action is to be quantified was never answered, because these constructs suggested dimensions to which the quantitative practices of science in general could not be applied.

3) In his emphasis upon the genesis of behavior, Freud made extensive use of processes of learning. These were never treated operationally in terms of changes in behavior but rather as the acquisition of ideas, feelings, and emotions later to be expressed by, or manifested in, behavior. Consider, for example, Freud's own suggestion that sibling rivalry in his own early history played an important part in his

theoretical considerations as well as in his personal relationships as an adult.

An infant brother died when Freud himself was only 1½ years old, and as a young child Freud played with a boy somewhat older than himself and presumably more powerful, yet who was, strangely enough, in the nominally subordinate position of being his nephew. To classify such a set of circumstances as sibling rivalry obscures, as we have seen, the many specific properties of the circumstances themselves regarded as independent variables in a science of behavior. To argue that *what was learned* was the effect of these circumstances upon unconscious or conscious aggressive tendencies or feelings of guilt works a similar misrepresentation of the dependent variable. An emphasis upon behavior would lead us to inquire into the specific acts plausibly assumed to be engendered by these childhood episodes. In very specific terms, how was the behavior of the young Freud *shaped* by the special reinforcing contingencies arising from the presence of a younger child in the family, by the death of that child, and by later association with an older playmate who nevertheless occupied a subordinate family position? What did the young Freud *learn to do* to achieve parental attention under these difficult circumstances? How did he avoid aversive consequences? Did he exaggerate any illness? Did he feign illness? Did he make a conspicuous display of behavior that brought commendation? Was such behavior to be found in the field of physical prowess or intellectual endeavor? Did he learn to engage in behavior that would in turn increase the repertoires available to him to achieve commendation? Did he strike or otherwise injure young children? Did he learn to injure them verbally by teasing? Was he punished for this, and if so, did he discover other forms of behavior that had the same damaging effect but were immune to punishment?

We cannot, of course, adequately answer questions of this sort at so late a date, but they suggest the kind of inquiry that would be prompted by a concern for the *explicit shaping of behavioral repertoires* under childhood circumstances. What has survived through the years is not aggression and guilt, later to be manifested in behavior, but rather patterns of behavior themselves. It is not enough to say that this is "all that is meant" by sibling rivalry or by its effects upon the mental apparatus. Such an expression obscures, rather than illuminates, the nature of the behavioral changes taking place in the childhood learning process. A similar analysis could be made of processes in the fields of motivation and emotion.

4) An explicit treatment of behavior as a datum, of probability of response as the principal quantifiable property of behavior, and of learning and other processes in terms of changes of probability is usually enough to avoid another pitfall into which Freud, in common with his contemporaries, fell. There are many words in the layman's vocabulary that suggest the activity of an organism yet are not descriptive of behavior in the narrower sense. Freud used many of these freely—for example, the individual is said to discriminate, remember, infer, repress, decide, and so on. Such terms do not refer to specific acts. We say that a man discriminates between two objects when he behaves differently with respect to them; but discriminating is not itself behavior. We say that he represses behavior which has been punished when he engages in other behavior *just because* it displaces the punished behavior; but repressing is not action. We say that he decides upon a course of conduct either when he enters upon the course to the exclusion of another, or when he alters some of the variables affecting his own behavior in order to bring this about; but there is no other "act of deciding." The difficulty is that when one uses terms which suggest an activity, one feels it necessary to invent an actor, and the subordinate personalities in the Freudian mental apparatus do, indeed, participate in just these activities rather than in the more specific behavior of the observable organism.

Among these activities are conspicuous instances involving the process of self-control—the so-called "Freudian mechanisms." These need not be regarded as activities of the individual or any subdivision thereof—they are not, for example, what happens when a skillful wish evades a censor—but simply as ways of representing relationships among responses and controlling variables. I have elsewhere tried to demonstrate this by restating the Freudian mechanisms without reference to Freudian theory (*4*).

5) Since Freud never developed a clear conception of the behavior of the organism and never approached many of the scientific problems peculiar to that subject matter, it is not surprising that he misinterpreted the nature of the

observation of one's own behavior. This is admittedly a delicate subject, which presents problems which no one, perhaps, has adequately solved. But the act of self-observation can be represented within the framework of physical science. This involves questioning the reality of sensations, ideas, feelings, and other states of consciousness which many people regard as among the most immediate experiences of their life. Freud himself prepared us for this change. There is, perhaps, no experience more powerful than that which the mystic reports of his awareness of the presence of God. The psychoanalyst explains this in other ways. He himself, however, may insist upon the reality of certain experiences that others wish to question. There are other ways of describing what is actually seen or felt under such circumstances.

Each of us is in particularly close contact with a small part of the universe enclosed within his own skin. Under certain limited circumstances, we may come to react to that part of the universe in unusual ways. But it does not follow that that particular part has any special physical or non-physical properties or that our observations of it differ in any fundamental respect from our observations of the rest of the world. I have tried to show elsewhere (4) how self-knowledge of this sort arises and why it is likely to be subject to limitations that are troublesome from the point of view of physical science. Freud's representations of these events was a particular personal contribution influenced by his own cultural history. It is possible that science can now move on to a different description of them. If it is impossible to be wholly nonmetaphorical, at least we may improve upon our metaphors.

The crucial issue here is the Freudian distinction between the conscious and unconscious mind. Freud's contribution has been widely misunderstood. The important point was not that the individual was often unable to describe important aspects of his own behavior or identify important causal relationships but that his ability to describe them was irrelevant to the occurrence of the behavior or to the effectiveness of the causes. We begin by attributing the behavior of the individual to events in his genetic and environmental history. We then note that because of certain cultural practices, the individual may come to describe some of that behavior and some of those causal relationships. We may say that he is conscious of the parts he can describe and unconscious of the rest. But the act of self-description, as of self-observation, plays no part in the determination of action. It is superimposed upon behavior. Freud's argument that we need not be aware of important causes of conduct leads naturally to the broader conclusion that awareness of cause has nothing to do with causal effectiveness.

In addition to these specific consequences of Freud's mental apparatus in obscuring important details among the variables of which human behavior is a function and in leading to the neglect of important problems in the analysis of behavior as a primary datum, we have to note the most unfortunate effect of all. Freud's methodological strategy has prevented the incorporation of psychoanalysis into the body of science proper. It was inherent in the nature of such an explanatory system that its key entities would be unquantifiable in the sense in which entities in science are generally quantifiable, but the spatial and temporal dimensions of these entities have caused other kinds of trouble.

One can sense a certain embarrassment among psychoanalytic writers with respect to the primary entities of the mental apparatus. There is a predilection for terms that avoid the embarrassing question of the spatial dimensions, physical or otherwise, of terms at the primary level. Although it is occasionally necessary to refer to mental events and their qualities and to states of consciousness, the analyst usually moves on in some haste to less committal terms such as *forces, processes, organizations, tensions, systems,* and *mechanisms.* But all these imply terms at a lower level. The notion of a conscious or unconscious "force" may be a useful metaphor, but if this is analogous to force in physics, what is the analogous mass that is analogously accelerated? Human behavior is in a state of flux and undergoing changes that we call "processes," but what is changing in what direction when we speak of, for example, an affective process? Psychological "organizations," "mental systems," "motivational interaction"—these all imply arrangements or relationships among *things,* but what are the things so related or arranged? Until this question has been answered the problem of the dimensions of the mental apparatus can scarcely be approached. It is not likely that the problem can be solved by working out independent units appropriate to the mental apparatus, although it has been proposed to undertake such a step in attempting to place psychoanalysis on a scientific footing.

Before one attempts to work out units of transference or scales of anxiety, or systems of mensuration appropriate to the regions of consciousness, it is worth asking whether there is not an alternative program for a *rapprochement* with physical science that would make such a task unnecessary. Freud could hope for an eventual union with physics or physiology only through the discovery of neurological mechanisms that would be the analogs of, or possibly only other aspects of, the features of his mental apparatus. Since this depended upon the prosecution of a science of neurology far beyond its current state of knowledge, it was not an attractive future. Freud appears never to have considered the possibility of bringing the concepts and theories of a psychological science into contact with the rest of physical and biological science by the simple expedient of an operational definition of terms. This would have placed the mental apparatus in jeopardy as a life goal, but it would have brought him back to the observable, manipulable, and preeminently physical variables with which he was in the last analysis dealing.

NOTES

1. E. Jones, *Life and Work of Sigmund Freud* (Basic Books, New York, 1953), vol. 1.
2. E. Frenkel-Brunswik, p. 97 ff.
3. Although it was Freud himself who taught us to doubt the face value of introspection, he appears to have been responsible for the view that another sort of direct experience is required if certain activities in the mental apparatus are to be comprehended. Such a requirement is implied in the modern assertion that only those who have been psychoanalyzed can fully understand the meaning of transference or the release of a repressed fear.
4. B. F. Skinner, *Science and Human Behavior* (Macmillan, New York, 1953).

The Scientific Status of Psychoanalysis

by Jerome Richfield

FROM THE TIME of the well-known polemic by Knight Dunlap in 1920 to the recent publication of the Hixon lectures on *Psychoanalysis as Science* (*1*), much energy has been expended, and perhaps dissipated, in an effort to determine the so-called "scientific status of psychoanalysis." This paper is primarily an attempt at a brief consideration of some of the problems underlying such efforts. I wish to suggest that the questions and statements ordinarily involved in discussions of the relationship between psychoanalysis and science are arbitrary, confused, and inadequate. I hope to show that the problem of the scientific status of psychoanalysis needs restatement.

Discussions of psychoanalysis as a science differ in at least one significant respect from discussions of, say, physics as a science. When psychoanalysis is discussed in this connection, the questions asked are aimed at a supposed need of determining whether psychoanalysis is fundamentally and genuinely scientific, but when physics is discussed the questions are aimed at discovering the nature of science itself. Thus, whether or not psychoanalysis is deterministic has been considered a factor in evaluating its status as a science. Yet in quantum physics, the limitation set by Heisenberg's relationship on any strict application of the principle of causality has resulted in the judgment that *science* is no longer deterministic (*2*). There is no special difficulty in this particular difference between the two fields except for its effect upon the philosophic consideration of questions about the scientific status of psychoanalysis.

In our present culture, such questions are important because of the eulogistic function, or emotive significance, of the term *science*. It seems to be assumed that to question the *scientific* status of an activity is equivalent to asking whether that activity is desirable, reliable, and valid.

The disinterested opponents of psychoanalysis usually find the ground for their repudiations in a discrepancy between some aspect of psychoanalysis and some concept of science. The scientific character of psychoanalysis has been impugned on the ground that, as a dynamic theory of human behavior, it is deterministic, although man is not a machine. And psychoanalysis has also been assailed as unscientific because it formulates motive explanations instead of restricting itself to the causal type of statement attributed to the orthodox determinism of neurophysiology and biochemistry.

While one commentator claims that there are only two accounts of psychosomatic sequences that have scientific status, because these alone reveal the attention to mechanism that he requires of any theory (3), another describes the vastly diminished importance of mechanical explanation in contemporary science and holds that such attempts at explanation are a Victorian remnant which recent events in physics have shown to be impossible or undesirable (4).

Most critics have agreed very little on whether the chief difficulty with the scientific character of psychoanalysis should be said to be its limitations in the way of controlled experimentation, its relative lack of predictive ability, its difficulties in the way of quantification and measurement, its extraordinary profusion of variables, the complexity of its terminological innovations, its paucity of statistical correlations, the existence of broad theoretical schisms among its practitioners, the subjectivity of many of its data, the metaphorical character of its basic terms, the role of the investigator's personality as an intervening variable, the absence of operational definitions, or, in general, the failure of psychoanalysis to resemble physics in significant respects.

It should not be surprising that this bewildering array of diverse criteria results from questions about "the scientific status" of any field. Although these questions are regularly phrased in familiar terms, it does not seem to have been sufficiently appreciated that the common unexplicated use of a term presupposes a common acceptance of its meaning. *Science* and *psychoanalysis* are terms of varying applicability. Neither has both a fixed and a definite denotation. Both terms are to be found in controversial uses. Many statements that involve the terms *science* and *the scientific method* have no clear sense, no unambiguous use. And since the term *scientific* has a mixed descriptive and evaluative, or prescriptive, function, the ostensibly simple questions about the relationship of psychoanalysis and science take for granted a variety of preconceptions that need to be justified.

Questions about the nature of science are not scientific questions; they are not like those concerned with the nature of zebras, falling bodies, electrons, and physiological functions. They are questions that involve a technical philosophic analysis in terms of some combination of sociological, semantic, ethical, logical, epistemological, and historical facts and values.

Perhaps it is not the privilege or the responsibility of the philosopher to make very many of the prescriptions that would be entailed by a critical use of the term *scientific*. But it is a necessary and characteristic philosophic activity to disclose the existence and significance of these prescriptions through an analysis of the actual uses of the term.

First, it should be recognized that determinations of scientific status always involve the use of certain arbitrary stipulations in the way of meaning. This may be clearly seen in a consideration of a few of the historical objections that have been made against psychoanalysis.

One old and persistent charge against psychoanalysis compares it with mysticism (5). The argument here depends upon the proposition that knowledge is of two kinds, perceptual and inferential. Mysticism is defined as the belief in the cognitive function of some third kind of experience which is rejected by the non-mystic as being simply emotional. When it is noted that many psychoanalytic data are derived from certain empathic processes, such as the so-called "transference relationship" between patient and analyst, it is argued that the result can be only the mystical third kind of experience and cannot be taken account of by what is deemed "genuine science."

The statement that knowledge is either perceptual or inferential must itself be either a proposition of logic or an empirical finding. In the first case, the denial of cognitive significance to any emotional process would result from a trivial tautology. And whether or not the determination to use the word *knowledge* in this way is conventionalized, it is inconsistent with the professed aims of scientists, since it logically precludes certain factual investigations.

If the statement is intended to describe a factual discovery and is not an *a priori* legislation, then psychoanalysis cannot be judged unscientific merely on the ground that some of its statements are functions of certain affective relationships. The psychoanalyst might explain the so-called "empathic understanding" as a kind of ordinary perception, or he might claim to have, in fact, some third kind of knowledge that is neither perceptual nor inferential. In either case, the usefulness of the empathic technique does not depend upon its explanation. The question is whether testable hypotheses are obtainable from the characteristic activities of the psychoanalyst, and not whether the psychoanalyst, like the mystic, assigns a cognitive function to various emotional states.

Some traditional objections to psychoanalysis, although not themselves suffering from faulty logical or semantic formulation, depend upon certain unfortunate ways in which some psychoanalysts express their hypotheses. It has been said repeatedly that various psychoanalytic hypotheses violate a fundamental canon of scientific method to the effect that statements must be expressed in a manner that allows for the possibility of disproof. Here the rule is entirely acceptable. We cannot be said to be making a significant assertion if its falsity is inconceivable. Do psychoanalysts commit this error? It does appear from some psychoanalytic statements that human behavior is divided between pathological excesses and their reaction formations. It has been shown that psychoanalysts will support the concept of an anal character by citing studies "which found a higher frequency of reported stinginess, and *also of extravagance* among adults who confessed to a recall of some form of anal eroticism" (6).

Critics have claimed that these examples of psychoanalytic statements violate our methodological canon in arguing "that *opposite* traits reveal the *same* underlying condition." Despite the apparent plausibility of this important criticism, it can readily be shown that the objection involved does not apply. The characteristic psychoanalytic hypotheses that concern us here are highly elliptical statements concealing much theoretical complexity. We should not understand the psychoanalyst to be asserting simply that the concept of an anal character implies stinginess in one case and extravagance in another. What is intended is the statement that an anal character, together with certain variables, implies stinginess in one case, while an anal character with *different* variables in another instance implies extravagance.

In some cases, the so-called "opposite" traits, which are held to reveal "the same underlying condition," are not real contraries. And their logical incompatibility in the same hypotheses is apparent only. The psychoanalyst will relate both extravagance and stinginess to an anal character by analyzing extravagance into denied stinginess. The difficulty arises when the single term *stingy* is used indifferently in referring to certain modified impulses as well as to various instances of overt behavior. The patient who hoards and the patient who reacts with extravagant behavior to his primary impulse to hoard are not "stingy" in the same sense. This is very often obscured by the psychoanalytic statement that the extravagant patient is "really" stingy.

It is frequently objected that psychoanalysis has not yet exceeded the outmoded level of nineteenth century biology in its use of the concept of instinct, or instinctual drive, as a basic explanatory mechanism.

There is no question that psychoanalysts use the term *instinct* and its cognates extensively. But let us question this usage to determine whether any more is ordinarily involved in its psychoanalytic meaning than some unspecified analogic function. Most psychoanalysts do not believe that there are any basic biological forces that manifest themselves in human behavior independently of the influences and conditioning of a variety of environmental factors. They deal with the concept of a kind of mental phenomenon experienced directly as an "urging energy," which, in combination with certain external stimuli, will lower the excitation level of the organism through the discharge of tension.

These urges have some of the characteristics associated with the biological notion of instinct. But they differ in significant respects. The primary urges referred to in psychoanalytic literature are neither biologically inherited nor unalterable in the face of such external stimuli as social, economic, and political factors.

From the point of view of the semanticist, it is unfortunate that psychoanalysts use the word *instinct*. But this does not falsify any psychoanalytic correlations or invalidate the principle of the homeostatic model used in psychodynamic explanation.

We might hope to settle disagreements concerning the scientific status of psychoanalysis if we were to succeed first in producing a sufficiently *persuasive* definition of *science*. Then by examining psychoanalysis, we might note the extent of its conformity to this newly constructed denotation. But this procedure would not preclude the possibility, or even diminish the likelihood, of persistent and warranted dispute.

Suppose the following question arose: How much conformity is necessary before psychoanalysis should be awarded its scientific credentials? To show how this question of the degree of conformity might arise, let us consider briefly the problem of experimentation, an activity closely associated with the present vague notion of science and a characteristic of varied importance in most of the generally accepted special sciences.

Experimentation does take place within psychoanalytic psychiatry but not without certain difficulties and limitations that disinguish it from the experiments of the physicist or the chemist. First, most of the behavioral states involved in psychoanalytic study are not reproducible under laboratory conditions; yet experimentally designed conflict-situations and controlled study of various toxic psychoses can yield some analogous phenomena. The experimental psychoanalyst must make cautious inferences from these.

The psychoanalyst is limited as well by the fact that he himself is inescapably a part of the very subject of his investigations. The personality of the experimenter is one of the significant variables to be controlled. This does not make psychoanalytic experimentation unfeasible. In principle, at least, the integrity of the experimental subject can be preserved by interpreting all results in light of this factor of counter-transference. The principles involved in the interpretation of the transference are not peculiar to experimentation in psychoanalysis or devised expressly to resolve the experimental problem. They constitute the core of psychoanalytic therapy and are derived from basic psychoanalytic hypotheses.

Finally, in contrast to physics, which is an ahistorical science, psychoanalysis is often concerned with factors that gain their psychological significance at some particular point in the history of a personality. Even if the experimental simulation or reproduction of such a factor were possible, its action upon a different personality, or upon a different phase of the development of the same personality, would very likely be meaningless. It could not, then, be considered a requirement of systematic study.

It seems that there is neither a clearly justifiable basis nor any regularly accepted criterion for attempting to fix "the scientific status of psychoanalysis." Most methodological criticism of psychoanalysis has been a futile attempt to shape it more and more into a form that criticism within physics is incessantly changing. We should be explicit in recognizing that, if the general characteristics of what we now mean by *physics* are to determine the meaning of *science* and, therefore, the *scientific status* of another kind of investigation, discussions about science and psychoanalysis will have another complexion. For any question of the resemblance between psychoanalysis and physics does not, by itself, seem as important a matter as the present question of whether psychoanalysis is to be termed *scientific*. Thus, if the meaning of *science* is to be purely a pragmatic convention, determined and exclusively modified by the nature and problems of quantum physics then the question of psychoanalysis as science might be unworthy of our consideration. But if *science* is to mean, among other things, some distinctive ways in which men actually deal with their experiences, then it is the responsibility of the psychoanalyst to play a prominent role in the creation and development of scientific principles. Psychoanalysis cannot passively await the outcome of the convulsions that currently beset the philosophy of science.

The psychoanalyst should apply certain methodological norms and techniques of research when these are compatible with the nature of the facts upon which his work depends. He should not conform to certain procedures simply because they are characteristic of a highly regarded physics or are in some questionable way associated with a vague and arbitrary abstraction like the general notion of "science."

The term *scientific method* is at present clearest and most useful when it is taken as a historical expression, designating the class of different procedures that men in search of systematic factual knowledge have found best suited to the realization of their goal. Any further specification would be groundless and productive of nothing except endless dispute.

NOTES

1. Stanford Univ. Press, Calif. (1952).
2. See, for example, M. Schlick, *Philsosophy of Nature* (Philosophical Library, New York, 1940), p. 70.
3. J. O. Wisdom, *Brit. J. Med. Psychol.* **26** (1953), pt. I, p. 15.
4. M. Johnson, *Science and the Meanings of Truth* (Faber & Faber, London, 1946).
5. See K. Dunlap, *Mysticism, Freudianism and Scientific Psychology* (Mosby, St. Louis, 1920).
6. R. E. L. Faris, *Am. Sociol. Rev.* **18**, 438 (1953).

Notes on the Discussion Between

E. Frenkel-Brunswik and B. F. Skinner

by Michael Scriven

A NUMBER of interesting points have been raised by the first two papers in this symposium, but I wish to contain myself to examining one point which I think represents the fundamental issue between them. It is this: Does the theoretical aspect of psychoanalytic discussion contribute anything useful over and above the admittedly important observed correlations (for example, between specified types of trauma and neuroses)?

Now, it might be possible to settle the matter by appealing to the evidence—by showing that diagnoses based on the theory are therapeutically superior to those based only on knowledge of the correlations. But even if this was the appropriate place for such a discussion, most of us realize that it would not be conclusive. Moreover, it would not go to the heart of the matter: for Dr. Skinner disagrees in a fundamental way with the method involved rather than with the actual results of the method. He does not believe that the process of hypothesizing in a new theoretical language is ever fruitful.

It seems to me that there are two weaknesses in this position. First, I would disagree on historical grounds. I believe that the suggestive power of conceptual terms is indispensable to scientific activity; and I do not think that this can be dismissed as a property of an immature science—it seems to me to be what distinguishes a science from a summary. In fact, it seems quite evident to me that many of the great steps in the history of science have not only followed the sudden perception of familiar events in a new way, according to a new model—in short, as a result of a new hypothesis —but that they could not have been made otherwise, for example, Lavoisier with the theory of combustion, Kepler with the planetary motions, Guericke and the spring of the air, and Freud and the unconscious wish—these were new ways of interpreting correlations, not new correlations. But, of course, they immediately *led* to new correlations, which makes the Skinnerian interpretation of history more plausible at first sight than a precise chronological account leaves it. Further consideration of the historical point leads one to look for a reason for the importance of hypothetical concepts, which forms the second and more important of my two arguments against Skinner. It is a logical point rather than an empirical one.

I do not think that there is a fundamental difference between the observation terms and the theoretical terms of science, even at a given moment. There are *important* differences, indeed, between terms such as "length" or "response frequency," on the one hand, and others such as "entropy" or "intelligence." But it is a mistake to think that these differences correspond to the difference between theory-neutral and theory-contaminated terms. For observation terms are also embedded in a theory, albeit a very well-established one, and every now and again we are awakened by the discovery that this theory is not inviolable and that we have to change our concept of let us say, length in a fundamental way, perhaps by introducing a reference to the velocity of the measured object. Conversely, although we may observe entropy changes or intelligence levels in a different way from length and response frequency—a way that makes people want to say that we really *infer* them from other observations—this is only half the truth, for we do *observe* that a man is intelligent or introverted or unconsciously motivated. So the distinction between psychoanalytic explanation using Freudian language and quoting the correlations between behavior observations cannot be regarded as very fundamental—although I do not wish to deny that insofar as Freudian language is ambiguous, vague, or even inconsistent in application, it is less satisfactory in these respects than the comparatively simple (and less potentially fruitful) language of overt behavioral observations.

I find it difficult to say anything much more precise than this on the issue. Skinner takes a rather elusive position; once we have conceded to him that psychoanalytic theory is far from precise, containing perhaps very few concepts that are pragmatically valuable, and he has agreed with us (as he has done elsewhere) that "botanizing" is not enough in behavior science—that more is involved than the comparatively simple sort of correlations that form the basis of a classificatory system—then we find it hard to locate an unambiguous position for him between these alternatives. Perhaps we can best understand his attitude in terms of his own practice. He is not, in my understanding, primarily interested in the explanation of behavior but rather in providing the descriptive laws that form an important part of explanations. To bring an old and rather worn distinction into service, Skinner's interest appears to be in answering the "how" rather than the "why" about behavior. I do not wish to claim here that there is an absolutely fundamental difference between the answers to these questions, but there is at least a difference of level in the explanation, and this amounts to saying that the generalizations involved in the answer to the "why" question can be used to deduce more results than those connected with the "how" question. The answer to "why" requires at least a law of sufficient generality to subsume under it the law that describes "how." Now the area in which Skinner works, investigating one particular type of response under a few particular types of motivation and conditioning in a few organisms, is certainly an area where the "how" question needs answering and it may be done—given experimental ingenuity and perseverance—within a very simple theoretical structure. Almost, in fact, within the theoretical structure of ordinary observation-of-behavior language. But even in such an area there can be people who try, not to find, but to explain once found, the form of the regularities. Their quest is surely legitimate although certainly sometimes premature. And so the process continues, perhaps not unilaterally, perhaps establishing linkages in many different directions, toward engineering and algebra as well as toward neurophysiology. But this process cannot continue without bridging the gaps between the different levels of law, between the incommensurate units and models of different subjects; and one cannot bridge these gaps without hypotheses, concepts, and theoretical terms of which the Freudian vocabulary affords an interesting, though imperfect, example.

Chapter 4

Organism and Machine

Direction of Processes in Living Systems

by Wolfgang Köhler

OUR TOPIC, "Organism and machine," is clearly a short form of the following question. Can the functioning of organisms be explained in terms of the conditions and actions which are found in inanimate machines? It might at first appear that this question ought to be answered by experts in biology, namely, by anatomists, physiologists, and biochemists. Unfortunately, these experts are not inclined to deal with such general issues. If we were to ask a man who is now studying, say, the role of sodium ions in the transmission of nerve impulses, he would probably tell us to leave him, please, alone—that he has no time for speculation. Who would not sympathize with this scientist who likes to work on problems for which precise solutions can probably be found in the near future? On the other hand, specialists should not criticize us too severely if we are interested also in more general issues. For, if the behavior of sodium ions in the active nerve fiber were perfectly known, if we had discovered the last vitamin, and so forth, we should still have to ask why, taken together and interrelated, the various operations of the organism tend to preserve its existence as well as they do. Can this achievement be explained in terms of machine conceptions?

Actually, the philosophers of science and the theoretical physicists may be at lest as competent to clarify this issue as are the specialists in biology. I shall now try to indicate how these people might approach our problem.

The tendency of organisms to maintain themselves by their own processes is too obvious to need illustrations. But how are we to decide whether this tendency can be explained in machine terms, if we are not sure what we mean by a machine? Is just any part of inanimate nature a machine? Sometimes we talk as though we used the concept in this extremely wide sense. Even the physical universe as a whole may occasionally have been called a machine. The trouble is that the same term has also a much more specific meaning, and that, when discussing the topic "Organism and machine," we are for the most part not aware of this ambiguity. A machine in the more restricted sense is a physical system in which rigid arrangements or constraints compel events to take a certain course. In a well-constructed machine, this influence is one-sided. The constraints of the machine exclude all possibilities of action which would not be in line with the intended course; but, typically, the constraints cannot be altered by forces which action exerts on such solid conditions.

A simple example will make this clearer. One can easily compel an electric current to take a course which has the shape of a W. For this purpose, it will suffice to conduct the current through a rigid wire, part of which has this shape, and is kept in this shape by being firmly attached to a suitable support. There is nothing in a current as such that favors this particular shape. The form of a W is impressed upon the current only by the described arrangement. It is in this fashion that physical events are forced to follow prescribed ways in man-made machines.

We must next show that the form which a physical process assumes can also be determined in an entirely different manner. Take this example. A thoroughly flexible insulated wire which forms a closed curve is placed on a smooth and plane surface. At first, the curve may be given any arbitrarily chosen shape. This shape will at once be altered if now an electromotive force is induced in the wire so that a current is set up. The shape is changed by the magnetic field of this current, and the direction of the change is such that it enlarges the area surrounded by the conductor. Actually, the conductor may be transformed into a circle, the shape in which it circumscribes the greatest possible area.

The difference between this and the preceding example must be obvious. In the present situation, there are no particular constraints by which a special form of the conductor and the current is prescribed. Rather, it is the free dynamics of the system which brings about the change and determines its direction. Obviously, then, we have good reasons for distinguishing between these two factors on which the form of physical events in a system may depend: constraints, on the one hand, and directions inherent in the dynamics of the system, on the other hand. In a given instance, both factors may, of course, operate at the same time.

When trying to understand phenomena which exhibit a

striking order or show a persistent direction, man thinks more readily in terms of constraints by which such facts might be explained than in dynamic terms. Thus the remarkable order of movements in the translunar world was once explained by crystal spheres to which the stars were supposed to be attached. In this fashion they had to perform prescribed movements. Again, when Descartes tried to explain the order of organic processes, he began at once to think in terms of anatomical arrangements which enforce this order. It never occurred to him that, quite apart from such arrangements, directions inherent in biological dynamics might play a major part in the self-maintenance of living systems. Even in our time, it seems sometimes to be felt that, when the dynamics of a system is allowed to operate on its own, the result is likely to be chaos.

In typical inanimate machines, operations are constrained to take courses which serve human purposes. But systems may have the characteristics of machines without having been built by man. The crystal spheres of Aristotelian astronomy, for instance, were assumed to be of divine origin; and Descartes probably believed that the anatomy of organisms had been chosen by the Lord, who in this fashion made it possible for them to maintain themselves. In our time, evolution has taken the place of such agents. Evolution has, of course, no interests and no purposes. Nonetheless, if we follow Darwin, living systems tend to change in a particular direction, the direction in which their chances of survival are increased; for those that do not so change will soon succumb in the general competition inherent in living. But this does not explain the changes as such. What is their nature from the point of view of science? Darwin did not explain his theory in specific physical terms. In this respect, his work does not entirely satisfy the theorist of our time. However, his statements clearly imply that evolution changes mainly anatomical conditions; in other words, that it builds better and better arrangements by which organic events are forced to occur in biologically useful directions.

In this assumption, only one point seems to me open to criticism. Anatomical arrangements as such produce no action; they merely modify actions which occur for dynamic reasons. Consequently, the principles of dynamics cannot be ignored in a theory of evolution. But, actually, they are almost being ignored in this particular theory. Does the general principle of evolution contain any implications concerning the dynamics of organic processes? There is at least one such implication. In a strict theory of evolution, it must be assumed that evolution has changed no law of dynamics, and that it has introduced neither new forces nor new elementary processes. In this respect, the principle is therefore one of invariance rather than of change. Hence, in considering any *events* which occur in organisms, we have to think, first of all, of the laws of dynamics which are here involved. Presumably, these laws are still the same as they were before organisms appeared on this planet. Only as a second step can we then proceed to examine the particular conditions under which such laws now operate in given living systems.

Nobody will deny that, on the whole, histological facts serve to give organic events a useful form. The anatomy of the human eye, for instance, can hardly be described without referring to the use of this structure in clear visual perception. So numerous are examples of this kind that, without any doubt, organisms may to a large extent be regarded as machines in our more restricted sense of the term. Are we to conclude that living systems can be entirely explained in this fashion? Clearly, no such conclusion would be justified, because it can be shown that organisms maintain themselves, not only because of useful anatomical conditions in their interior, but also for reasons inherent in the principles of dynamics.

In the *first* place, we must remember a simple biological fact. It is true that certain anatomical arrangements force processes to take a course which helps the organism to survive. But what is the nature of such arrangements? Are they really comparable to the rigid constraints which we find in inanimate machines? In a most important sense, they are not. The very way in which they exist differs widely from the way in which constraints exist in machines. For the most part, such constraints consist of solid objects; they are composed of permanent materials which have been given one shape or another depending upon their particular purpose. On the other hand, no part of the anatomy of an organism is a permanent object. Rather, any such part must be regarded as a steady state, only the shape of which persists, while its material is all the time being removed and replaced by metobolic events. Surely, such steady states are fairly resistant and can, therefore, serve as constraining devices for more temporary functions. But from the point of view of our general topic, it is a most important fact that all organs, large or small, are processes rather than permanent objects. For it follows that any question concerning the useful course of those temporary functions must now be asked again with reference to the anatomical arrangements by which this course is enforced. If these arrangements are actually also processes, why is the form of *these* processes maintained for long periods, as it must be if the organism is to survive? It will hardly be suggested that the shape of the anatomical parts under consideration is maintained because there are further anatomical constraints which force metabolic events to operate in this fashion. For, what has just been said about the former anatomical arrangements would at once have to be repeated with regard to such hypothetical arrangements of a second order. They, too, would surely be steady forms of processes, rather than solid objects, and would therefore be subject to the same reasoning. Anybody who is familiar with the history of science will admit that, when theories take such a turn, something is probably wrong with basic premises.

At this point, some people take refuge in vitalism. I am not inclined to do so. It seems preferable now to consider a *second* reason which is opposed to an interpretation of organic events in machine terms alone. This reason is derived from physics. The organism would be a machine in the strict sense only if the behavior of *all* its parts were prescribed by special anatomical devices. Now this is clearly not the case. It will suffice if we mention one example. The distribution of the tissue fluid which pervades all parts of the body is not determined by particular devices. This continuum has, as the physicists would say, innumerable "degrees of freedom." To a large extent, its distribution is therefore a matter of dynamics. It follows that, if nevertheless this distribution tends to be favorable to survival, the self-maintaining conduct of the organism must be derived partly from a direction inherent in dynamics. Since the same consideration holds for other parts of the organism, principles of dynamics obviously play an important part in its self-maintenance.

This is my main point. From here, we should, of course,

proceed to a thorough examination of dynamics in general, in order to discover what directions it takes in systems of one kind or another. Unfortunately, knowledge in this field is so restricted that only a few remarks can be made at the present time.

What we learn from the physicists in this respect may be formulated as follows. If, in a closed system, macroscopic velocities are constantly being destroyed by friction, transformations in the system will be such that the sum of all energies capable of producing further transformations decreases. When these energies have reached a minimal amount, the system will no longer change. Although this is a perfectly good principle, it cannot, in its present formulation, be applied to the organism. For the organism is obviously not a closed system; moreover, while the direction indicated by the principle may be called "downward," the direction of events in healthy organisms is on the whole surely not "downward" but, in a good sense, "upward." Thus the energy content of a young organism generally increases, and when at times it spends more than it gains, events soon take a turn by which the loss is balanced, if not overbalanced. Nevertheless, no serious difficulty arises at this point, because the direction which events take in open systems need not be the same as that which they take in closed systems. In fact, events in some simple physical systems tend to develop "upward," just as does the energy content of a young organism. For instance, any fire which is locally started, and then grows or spreads, exhibits this behavior. It can do so because the first weak flame is in contact with combustible material and with the oxygen of the surrounding air, which together constitute a store of potential energy. In other words, the flame is an open system, and the closed system which must here be considered contains in addition this source of energy. For the closed system as a whole, it remains true that it must develop "downward." But it does not follow that the same must happen to the part of it in which we are interested, namely, the flame. For as soon as the fire is started, it begins to feed on the store of potential energy, so that its own energy grows.

It is quite possible that the same principle is involved when a young organism develops "upward." For, this organism is also an open system surrounded by stores of energy which it absorbs and spends in growing. Taken together, the food which it eats and the oxygen which it inhales constitute large amounts of energy. Only one point remains to be added. When a flame, say, that of a candle, has developed to maximal size, it maintains itself at this level so far as it can. Need we be surprised if, once an organism is fully developed, it maintains its vigor so far as circumstances permit?

I must confess that, although this reasoning may point in the right direction, it is, for my taste, too abstract and general. There are too many problems to which it does not refer at all. For instance, the fact that organisms are open systems does not protect them against illness or old age. In both situations their energy tends to decrease. Moreover, sooner or later organisms die, even if they are not injured by outside agents. This means, of course, that open systems *may* develop "upward," that they *may* maintain themselves in states of high vigor, but that they need not, and do not, do so under all circumstances. What, then, are the conditions under which the present principle works? When, on the other hand, will an open system deteriorate even though energy can be transferred to it from an outside store? So long as we cannot answer such questions, we are far from understanding the way in which living systems maintain themselves. As a further criticism, I should like to point out that between certain simple systems in physics, which develop "upward," and the organisms with their tremendous variety of operations there still remains an enormous gap. As a result, the behavior of the former does not help us very much when we try to clarify that of the latter.

Such shortcomings may, of course, be remedied in the future. Many physicists are now strongly interested in biological questions. It should not be difficult for them to discover under what circumstances open systems of the inanimate world show the "upward" trend, and under what others they do not. Moreover, such physicists might also investigate open systems which are not so simple as the flame of a candle. The most astounding characteristic of organisms is the fact that so many processes in their interior virtually seem to cooperate when, as a whole, they maintain the organism's existence. Let us hope that the problem which arises here can be solved with the conceptual tools of physics. But it must be admitted that at the present time the task still seems enormous. Even macroscopic physics is not yet a completed science. It has hardly begun to study the behavior of open systems.

Is the Concept of an Organism

as a Machine a Useful One?

by N. Rashevsky

HALF A CENTURY ago scientists used to evaluate their theories and theoretical concepts by asking the question: Is the theory or theoretical concept true or false? Since the days of Henri Poincaré the notion has gradually gained general ascendancy that the aforementioned criterion is not the proper one. In fact it is not even a meaningful criterion. Nowadays we do not ask whether a given theory or concept is true or false. We ask: Is it convenient or inconvenient; is it useful or not? The word *useful* is meant here not in the ordinary practical, utilitarian sense, which may enable the proverbial man in the street to translate it directly into dollars and cents. The convenience or usefulness of a theory or theoretical concept is measured by the savings it effects in our mental efforts, which are needed to correlate the theory with experience. It is the "economy of thought" that constitutes the measure of the usefulness or convenience of a theory.

To give an example, let us consider a generally known case from the history of physics. Even now, if one choose stubbornly to do so, it would be possible to explain all known physical phenomena from the point of view of the old concepts of absolute space, absolute time, and absolute motion. This can be done, provided that we are willing to pile up one *ad hoc* hypothesis upon other *ad hoc* hypotheses. But, except for velocities that are negligible as compared with the velocity of light, we would obtain a theoretical mess that no scientist could comprehend.

On the other hand, if we accept Einstein's ideas of relativity of space, time, and motion and use the concept of a four-dimensional space-time manifold, a number of complex phenomena receive a simple and mathematically elegant explanation. Each physical phenomenon falls, so to speak, naturally into its proper place. The economy of thought achieved is enormous. This is why we consider the classical concepts of space and time as generally inconvenient and useless, whereas we consider the relativistic concepts as very convenient and very useful.

There is another important criterion by which the contemporary scientist judges the usefulness or convenience of a theory or theoretical concept. A theory or theoretical concept is considered the more convenient or useful, the better it enables us to predict facts that hitherto have not been observed or that may have been observed but escaped notice. The history of the natural sciences is replete with such predictions. To mention only one, we can again refer to Einstein's theory of relativity, by means of which he predicted the deviation of light in the gravitational field of the sun, and the equivalence of mass and energy. The practical importance of the latter prediction does not require any discussion.

It is natural to ask the questions: How does the scientist make these predictions? What is it that sometimes gives to the scientist these peculiar oracular or prophetic powers? A great poet thought he could find the answer to this question in a highly poetical way. In Schiller's words:

> Mit dem Genius steht die Natur im ewigen Bunde;
> Wass der eine verspricht, leistet die andre gewiss.

As scientists, however, we can hardly be satisfied with this poetical explanation, and we must seek one that is more prosaic but also more scientific.

If we examine carefully the processes by means of which various predictions in the natural sciences have been made, we find that their mechanism works in the following manner. The scientist constructs theories, theoretical concepts, or theoretical frames of reference that are isomorphic with the world of observable phenomena. This isomorphism is never complete, never covers the whole range of observable phenomena. A complete isomorphism is the dream of the scientist. Whether this dream will ever come true is a question that I shall not discuss now. But the wider the range of isomorphism, the greater the predictive value of the theory. The isomorphism assigns, within a certain limited range, to each element of the conceptual framework a particular observable phenomenon, and to each relationship between the elements of the concept a particular relationship between the corresponding observable phenomena. The theory is "tested" by first verifying the correspondence between the elements of the conceptual framework and the *actually observed* phenomena. If the range of isomorphism exceeds the range of the phenomena actually observed, then the scientist can make predictions. He notices that in his conceptual structure there are elements to which no corresponding phenomena have yet been observed. Asuming that the isomorphism extends beyond the range of phenomena already observed (and this is a prerequisite of a good theory), he concludes that there must be in the surrounding world phenomena not yet observed and, from his conceptual framework, he deduces the relationships between those as yet unobserved phenomena. Within the range of isomorphism his prediction of new phenomena will come true. Outside of that range his predictions will fail.

The situation may be illustrated by means of a crude and inadequate example, which, however, brings home the essential point. Most of you doubtless have seen various ancient geographic maps, for instance, maps used by the ancient Greeks or Romans. The general outlines of the Greek peninsula and of the Italian "boot" were fairly accurately represented; to a lesser extent were the outlines of the North African shore; still less accurately, the outlines of the western Mediterranean. Beyond those limits many ancient maps are ludicrously fantastic.

A map is good and useful only when it is isomorphic to the actual terrain that it symbolically represents. Thus within the relatively small range, confined to the Greek and Apennine penisulas, those ancient maps were fairly good. An individual who never traveled before and who set forth on a long journey could, with the use of such a map, find out fairly accurately what type of terrain he would meet on his travels. In a very broad sense, he thus could "predict" some of his future experiences. But this would be possible only provided that he did not travel too far beyond Greece or Italy. If he attempted to circumnavigate Africa or travel into the

Baltic Sea, his map would be utterly useless, and he would be up against all sorts of "unpredicted" suprises.

It should not be thought that the conceptual structures of the scientist can represent only strictly causal relationships. They can just as well represent the probalistic relationships that are so frequently observed in modern physics and in other natural sciences. Instead of being characterized by the statement: "Element *a* stands in such and such relation to element *b*," the conceptual framework may be characterized by the statement: "The probability that element *a* stands in such and such relationship to element *b* is so and so." An excellent example of this type of conceptual framework is offered by the theory of random nets, as developed by Anatol Rapaport and his students in connection with their studies in the mathematical theories of the brain.

Thus the discovery of conceptual structures that are isomorphic to the observable world is the prime function of the theoretician. It was the great achievement of Einstein to have noticed that physical phenomena are within a wide range isomorphic to geometric relationships in a four-dimensional non-Euclidean hyperspace.

Now let us come to the subject of this discussion: the organism and the machine. From the old point of view, we could have asked the question: Is the organism a machine or not? That such a question is meaningless can be particularly well seen in this example. The answer to the question depends on the difinitions of the words *organism,* and *machine.* I submit that organism has not yet been defined in a way that satisfies all the criterions of a good definition given in the textbooks of logic. Doubtless we shall all agree that every one of us is an organism. If this were summertime, I might notice on a window a crawling fly or a mosquito. Again we will all agree that this is an organism. A plant in a flowerpot on the windowsill also is undoubtedly an organism. We also would all agree that the mildly pathogenic bacteria deep down in my throat, which cause me to cough occasionally, are organisms. But when we come to viruses, opinions divide, and there is still no general agreement on whether or not they are organisms. I submit that this lack of agreement is an indication of lack of a proper definition of an organism.

Now let us turn our attention to the concept of machine. Most people understand by machine a man-made contraption, which performs certain functions that serve a *preconceived purpose* of its inventor or maker. Among the Greeks there were those who defined a machine somewhat differently, speaking of a contraption of divine creation. In any case a personal purposeful creator was implied.

In the light of these definitions, let us now examine what we should do to answer *scientifically* the question of whether an organism is a machine. I insist on the word *scientifically*, meaning that we should use only evidence that withstands the acid test of scientific reliability. It is clear that we must ascertain, *by scientific methods,* the existence or nonexistence of a personal creator for any organism. I submit that if we ever begin to follow this path of inquiry, we shall have left the domain of the scentific before anyone can say "Jack Robinson." Thus in this case, as in all others, the old approach is shown to be useless and even meaningless.

From the point of view of the contemporary approach we may, however, legitimately ask the question: Is a particular, specified organism, or a clearly specified part thereof isomorphic to a given specified machine? This question is meaningful and can be answered either in the affirmative or in the negative. We shall now show by several examples that *within a small, sharply circumscribed range,* the answer to the question is *Yes.* We shall also see that therefore, *within that range,* the concept of a machine as a structure isomorphic to certain organisms, or parts thereof, is useful.

A crude analogy has been noticed between the heart and the vascular system on one hand, and a pump and system of pipes on the other. On the basis of this crude analogy some equally crude quantitative relationships have been deduced. Crude as they are, they have been very roughly confirmed by experiment. With the refinement of the mechanical analogy and with the complications of the conceptual picture, more refined relationships have been derived, and the agreement between theory and experiment has been considerably improved.

A particularly interesting example is offered by the development of various electronic computors. These machines perform complex tasks that hitherto have been the function of certain parts of our brain. Thus we may say that the electronic computors are, *with respect to their functions,* isomorphic with a small part of the human brain. We may legitimately ask whether this isomorphism extends also to *structure*. The answer to this *in general* is *No,* because neither an electronic tube nor a transistor is structurally isomorphic to a neuron. In *some* structural aspects the answer may well be *Yes*. It is quite possible that in the topology of the interconnections between different elements of a computor and different elements of the brain, an isomorphism, or rather a homeomorphism, is at hand. Studies in the mathematical biology of the central nervous system have sometimes proved useful in the design of some machines. Conversely, the designers of the electronic computors may give some highly useful suggestions to the mathematical biologists.

The third example is from a field of mathematical biology to which I have made a modest and rather inadequate contribution. I have in mind the theory of form of plants and animals, considered as optimal structures for the performance of given biological functions. For example, by considering the trunk of some quadrupeds as a beam supported at its two ends, we can derive from this mechanical analogy some approximate relationships between the gross length and width of the trunk and its mass. Such relationships have been found to agree roughly with actual data. Other mechanical analogies lead to expressions between the mass of the heart and the heart frequency, and the total mass of the animal. Analogous expressions have been derived for the size of lungs and the frequency of breathing, as related to the overall mass of the animal. They all agree roughly with the data that are available.

One of our brilliant students, David Cohn, has recently applied this approach to the structure of the vascular system. He has derived theoretical relationships that determine such quantities as the diameters of the main arteries, the average number of branchings in different size arteries, the average number and size of capillaries. The agreement between the theoretical expressions and available data is quite remarkable.

Thus we see that the notion of isomorphism between certain parts of some organisms and definite mechanical or electromechanical structures may be quite useful. How far should this approach be pushed? Only the future can tell. My personal feeling, and this is nothing but a feeling, with which anyone is just as likely to agree as to disagree, is this: Although in certain parts of biology, as, for example, some aspects of form, the mechanical analogies are likely to prove very fruitful, I do not think that the future of biology lies in too strong an emphasis of the analogies between organisms and machines. Some of the reasons for this feeling are the same as have been discussed by Wolfgang Köhler. It also seems to me that if we are to map successfully complex organisms upon some complex electromechanical structures, we will have to be guided in our design of those structures by our biological knowledge, thus creating a logical circle. To whatever concept biological phenomena will be found to be isomorphic, I do think it will be different and more general than that of a machine. Biology is still awaiting its Einstein, who by a stroke of genius will map the complex organismic phenomena onto a known physicochemical, physicomathematical, or purely mathematical structure.

Mysterium Iniquitatis—of Sinful Man

Aspiring into the Place of God

by Warren S. McCulloch

D'ARCY THOMPSON used to tell of his encounter with a biologist who had described a nearly spherical diatom bounded entirely by hexagons thus:

"But," I said, "Euler showed that hexagons alone cannot enclose a volume." To which the innominate biologist retorted, "That proves the superiority of God over mathematics."

Euler's proof happened to be correct, and the observations inaccurate. Had both been right, far from proving God's superiority to logic, they would have impugned his wit by catching him in a contradiction. Our first concern is to avoid the impropriety of such solecisms.

Our second resembles it slightly. Newton, Jeans, and Planck have used "God" to account for things they could not explain. Biologists, ignorant of mechanisms underlying functions, have introduced "Nature," "Vital Force," "Nervous Energy," "the Unconscious," or some other pseudonym

for God. Each of these supposititious explanations, to quote
Sir Thomas Browne, "puts the honest Father to the refuge
of a miracle."

Today no biological process is fully understood in terms
of chemistry and physics. The facts are unknown to us. Few
chemical properties are yet reduced to the physical relations
of atomic constituents. The mathematics is too cumbersome.
Physics itself wants a unified field theory and doubts determinism in atomic processes.

So much for Comte's hierarchical unity of science! At last
we are learning to admit ignorance, suspend judgment, and
forego the *explicatio ignoti per ignotium*—"God"—which
has proved as futile as it is profane. Instead we seek mechanisms, for two purposes.

Let us consider them one at a time. As soon as we devise
a machine that will do what has to be explained, we divest
the superstitious of any seeming warrant to his miracle. It is
enough to show that, if certain physical things were as-
sembled in a certain way, then, by the laws of physics, the
assemblage would do what is required of it. So imaginary
engines led Carnot to entropy and Maxwell to his electromagnetic equations, instead of to miracles. Both machines,
to their inventors, were more than metaphors for mathematics. But actual engines proved Carnot's a homolog,
whereas the elastic ether's being chimerical left Maxwell's
a mere analog. Yet, because each showed there could be a
machine that turned the trick, it were best to see them—at
least from the logical point of view—as existential devices.

By these means biologists have exorcised ghosts from the
body, whence they went to the head, like bats to the belfry.
To drive them thence, my mentor, Pike, spent his life replac-
ing them by simple engines to ring all the changes on the
chimes. He looked on the evolution of the nervous system,
on its ontogeny, on learning, even on reflexes, as spontaneous variants that survive in the competition to trap available
energy and thus secure energetic *Lebensraum* in the entropic
degeneration of sunshine to the *Wärmetod*. Whether atomic
or molecular chaos produces a sport, its thanks are due to
chance, not to divine intervention in its behalf. These notions
do not constitute mechanistic hypotheses but exhort us to
construct them. Call them metaphysical if you will—in this
good sense, that they prescribe ways of thinking physically

about affairs mental and relegated to the whims of spirit manifold. I am of Pike's persuasion.

But most people have heard of cybernetics from Norbert Wiener or his followers. Narrowly defined, it is but the art of the helmsman, to hold a course by swinging the rudder so as to offset any deviation from that course. For this the helmsman must be so informed of the consequences of his previous acts that he corrects them—communication engineers call this "negative feedback"—for the output of the helmsman decreases the input to the helmsman. The intrinsic governance of nervous activity, our reflexes and our appetites exemplify this process. In all of them, as in the steering of the ship, what must return is not energy but information. Hence, in an extended sense, cybernetics may be said to include the timeliest applications of the quantitative theory of information.

The circuit in a servomechanism may include, as we hold it does in man's head, complicated machines of calculation. Turing showed that one having a finite number of parts and states, scanning, marking, and erasing one of four symbols at a time on an infinite tape, can compute any computable number. The first part of the tape serves to prescribe which number his general machine shall compute. Pitts and I showed that brains were Turing machines, and that any Turing machine could be made out of neurons. For this we used a calculus of atomic propositions subscripted for the time when all-or-none impulses signalized them in the relays constituting the net, or the machine. In brains the relays are neurons and the blueprint of the net is the anatomy of their connections.

Since Hilbert arithmetized logic, the calculation of any computable number is equivalent to deducing any conclusion that follows from a finite set of premises, or to detecting any figure in an input, or having any general idea that can be induced from our sensations. Existential operations can be introduced into our calculus by inserting in the net any circuitry that will secure invariants under groups of transformations. Memories, general ideas, and even Spinozistic consciousness, the idea of ideas, can thus be generated in robots. These robots, even simple ones having but half a dozen relays may, without inconsistency, show that circularity of preference, or of choice, called the value anomaly which—contra Plato—precludes a common measure of "the good."

Elsewhere I have shown that computing machines by playing chess may not merely learn to play better than their designers, as Ashby would have it, but that they may learn the rules of the game when these are given only ostensively. This insures their ability to generate their own ethic—not merely to be good, like the virtuous savage, because they are so made that they cannot break the rules, nor, like the gospeled or inspired, because they were so instructed by their fellows or their creator. Unlike solitaire, chess can be enjoyed only by a society of men or machines whose desire to play exceeds their desire to win. This is easily determined by connecting their two feedback loops in such a way that the former dominates the latter. I grant that these complicated machines resemble the elephant or some other "Colossus of Nature" rather than ants, within whose "narrow engines there is more curious mathematic; and the civility of these little citizens more neatly sets forth the wisdom of their Maker. . . ." Yet, that we can design ethical robots, who may even invent games more fun than chess, is enough to prove that man's moral nature needs no supernatural source. Darwin observed, but Spencer failed to note, that success in the game of life, and so survival, is "often most promoted by mutual assistance."

Hence the crucial question: Can machines evolve? John von Neumann suggests that we are familiar only with simple machines that can make only simpler ones, so that we suppose this is a general law, whereas, in fact, complicated ones can make others still more complicated. Given a suitable Turing machine, coupled to a duplicator of tape and to an assembler of parts from a common store, it could make one like itself, put in a duplicate of its own tape, and cut loose its replica ready to make a new one like itself. There are now two. Their number will double with each generation. Variations compatible with this reproduction, regardless of their sources, will lead to evolution; for, though simpler mutations must fail, some more complicated will survive. Von Neumann, Wheeler, and Quastler have computed the required complexity and find that, for general Turing machines to survive, they must be about as complex as a totipotent protein molecule, which is the simplest thing we know that does reproduce itself. Totipotent protein molecules are the littlest citizens. Man has not yet found their mechanical prescription. He has made amino acids by shaking together CO_2, NH_3 and H_2O in the light, and he has made polypeptides from amino acids. When he makes proteins by sticking these together he can better estimate the probability of their formation by chance in evolutionary epochs. If the civility of these little citizens only set forth an evolved efficiency in forestalling the *Wärmetod,* we may forego the astronomers' cry against their Maker:

> What? From insensate nothing to evoke
> A sensate something to resent the yoke
> Of unpermitted pleasure under pain
> Of everlasting punishment if broke:
> Oh, were that justice and His holy right.

Following Wiener we estimate the complexity of a machine or an organism to be the number of yes-or-no decisions —we call them bits of information—necessary to specify its organization. This is the logarithm (base 2) of the reciprocal of the probability of that state and, hence, its negative entropy.

But Wiener has forerunners as well as followers in Cambridge. Charles Peirce first defined "information," his "third kind of quantity," as "the sum of synthetical propositions in which the symbol is subject to predicate,' antecedent or consequent." Of Peirce's friends, Holmes, in his *Mechanism in Mind and Morals,* excuses only volition from the sway of mechanical causation; and James, in several places, attributes the vagaries of the will to chance. Perhaps a New England conscience may afford freedom to its neighbors' wills, as Donne says we give "souls unto women only to make them capable of damnation." But surely he is damned already whose frame and fortune foredoom his failure. That he is the machine at fault insures that he and his neighbors hold him responsible. The common law construes intention from the deed, and a windmill that kills a man is deodand. Every psychiatrist who cares for the well-being of his patient comes to look on a man's sins as his misfortune of birth or breeding and is glad that his self-righteous brethren cannot climb into God's mercy seat.

Sin, in its widest sense, is but to miss a mark; and surely most of us are too familiar with self-guiding missiles to doubt that we can endow them with computers and target-seeking servos whereby to hit or miss their prey. The components of these circuits are too gross and inefficient for us to package in a head what fills the nose of a V-2 rocket. But given miniature efficient relays comparable to neurons, we could build machines as small to process information as fast and multifariously as a brain. The hardest thing to match is man's storage of bits of incidental information, but we can put an upper bound on that. Following Craik's lead, man's acquisition of such information has been measured and never found to exceed a hundred bits per second of sustained reception. Were it 10 times more throughout his life, he could store no more than 10^{13} such bits. Heinz von Förster arrived at a similar figure by noting that the mean half-life of a trace in human memory is half a day, and the access to it over only 10^6 channels, with an access time of about 1 millisecond. Hence a man will come to equilibrium with far fewer traces than there are junctional buttons on our neurons. Moreover, von Förster showed that if, by regenerating traces, we retained some 5 per cent of all our uptake, the energy required for this remembering would be only a fraction of 1 per cent of that which flows through brains. This answers Bertrand Russell's only serious question about the peculiar causality of human thinking. Ashby, in his book, *Design for a Brain,* proposed a mechanism of adaptation that avoids the fallacy of simple location of a trace and makes the thing we are to seek in a given brain and its multiple locations depend upon the sequence of its learnings.

To the theoretical question, Can you design a machine to do whatever a brain can do? the answer is this: If you will specify in a finite and unambiguous way what you think a brain does do with information, then we can design a machine to do it. Pitts and I have proved this constructively. But can you say what you think brains do?

In 1953, in the symposium on consciousness of the Institute for the Unity of Science, Wilder Penfield used the term, as we do in forensic medicine, to mean precisely that his patient at a later date bore witness to what he also bore witness to as having happened then and there. Of course we can make machines do that. The questioner meant "Was the patient aware that it was he himself that did it?" which is self-consciousness, requiring but simple reflective circuitry. The physiologist would have settled the argument by defining "consciousness" to mean "responsiveness to present stimulation with a lag called latency"—a trait that few things lack!—but a psychoanalyst explained to me that "a patient is conscious of what he once felt only if at a later time he can verbalize it"—which is to say, "he is conscious of those things of which he says he is conscious"—and this requires only a machine that sometimes answers "yes" to this question. That is too easy; and if all we mean by consciousness is this ghost of half of mind-stuff, we may forget it all as just a pseudo-question. But I am sure that for every empirical scientist to whom existence is as primary as it is to a true Thomist, what lurks behind this ghostly facade is the old Aristotelian "substance." To Helmholtz, it appeared as the "*locus observandi*"; to Einstein as "the frame of reference of the observer"; to Russell as "the egocentric particular involved in denotation." For MacKay it yields the distinction between the languages of the observer and of the actor. Granted that we have objective knowledge of others, and substantial knowledge only of ourselves, this only proves us to be like every other thing, and divine, if you will, only as a part of all that exists. It does not demonstrate the metaphysical self-sufficient mind or soul with the unique property of perception. However one defines feeling, perception, consciousness, substantial knowledge—so the definition be finite and unambiguous—each and all are well within the tricky scope of circuitry. So much for the existential purport of machines!

Their second *raison d'etre* is to generate hypotheses. A mechanism that fits all our data is one of an infinite number of possible explanations of our findings. It always has properties disclosed by deduction and subject to the test of experience. It may even lead to an invention. Contemporary opinion, in Haldane's phrase, regards "every physical invention as a blasphemy and every biological invention as a perversion." This is less a matter of heresy than of "radical indecency." Plowing, milking, alcohol, coffee, tobacco, birth control, and artificial insemination are only the by-products of biological knowledge. The chromosome shuffling of Mendelian genes, which has stood the test longer than any other equally significant biological discovery, never offended our sensibilities, although it lets chance materially dictate our constitution. Only recently have we come to the data that set limits to the applicability of Mendel's law.

Each hypothesis predicts the outcome of numberless experiments. Hence, though no hypothesis can be proved, it may ultimately be disproved. A good one is so specific that it can be disproved easily. This requires a minimum of logical, or *a priori,* probability compatible with the data. I have sometimes boasted that my pet notion of the mechanism responsible for our seeing shape regardless of size was disproved by MacKay's experiment in my own laboratory. What grieves me is that neither I nor anyone else has so far imagined another specific mechanism to account for form-vision.

Perhaps in this "best of all possible worlds" neurophysiologists, like physicists, will be compelled to call their shots "on a cloth untrue, with a twisted cue and elliptical billiard balls." Russell has already noted that the explanation of mind has become more materialistic only as our matter has become less material. So we seem to be groping our way toward an indifferent monism. Everything we learn of organisms leads us to conclude not merely that they are analogous to machines but that they are machines. Man-made machines are not brains, but brains are a very ill-understood variety of computing machines. Cybernetics has helped to pull down the wall between the great world of physics and the ghetto of the mind.

Moreover, its analysis of nervous activity reveals two limits to our aspirations—our double ignorabimus. The impulses we receive from our receptors embody primary atomic propositions. Each impulse is an event. It happens only once. Consequently, these propositions are primary in the sense that each is true or else false, quite apart from the truth or falsity of any other. Were this not so, they would be redundant or, in the limit, as devoid of information as tautologies. But this means that the truth of each and every one cannot be tested. The empiricist, like the Thomist, must believe that God did not give him his senses in order to deceive him.

Moreover man, like his inventions, is subject to the second law of thermodynamics. Just as his body renders energy unavailable, so his brain corrupts the revelation of his senses. His output of information is but one part in a million of his input. He is a sink rather than a source of information. The creative flights of his imagination are but distortions of a fraction of his data.

Finally, as he has perforce learned from the inadequacies of his best hypotheses, ultimate universal truths are beyond his ken. To demand them is the arrogance of Adam; to come short of them is the impotence of sorry man; but to fancy them known were very ὕβρις. Obviously, he may know something about the past, although he cannot change it. The future he may affect, but he may never know it. Were this otherwise, he could beat the second law and build machines to operate on future information. So we may conclude that we fear no analogy between machines and organisms, either for existential purport or for generating hypotheses, and that we are safe to admit that organisms, even brains, are machines.

So long as we, like good empiricists, remember that it is an act of faith to believe our senses, that we corrupt but do not generate information, and that our most respectable hypotheses are but guesses open to refutation, so long may we "rest assured that God has not given us over to thraldom under that mystery of iniquity, of sinful man aspiring into the place of God."

Chapter 5

Science as a Social and Historical Phenomenon

Science During the French Revolution

by Henry Guerlac

THE late eighteenth century, including the period of the French Revolution, is a richly rewarding field of study for anyone concerned with the influence of science upon society, or with the impact of social change upon the work and thought of scientists. Never before, and rarely since, has science enjoyed such unalloyed esteem as it did in the Europe, especially the France, of the Age of Enlightenment, when it had for its advocates and propagandists the outstanding men of letters and social theorists from Montesquieu and Voltaire to Condorcet and Volney. Inspired by the writings of Descartes and Newton, these men drew confident arguments from the realm of physical law in their campaign to bring a similar rule of reason, law, and harmony into the inherited social institutions of their day. From science and its recent history, moreover, they took their most compelling examples of intellectual progress, finding support therein for their gilded vision of indefinite human perfectibility.

This favorable climate of opinion helps explain the mysterious concatenation of events discussed in this paper: the fact that the greatest period of French scientific leadership coincided almost precisely with the Age of Revolution; and that the time of Mirabeau, Danton, Robespierre, and Bonaparte was also, I need hardly point out, that of Lagrange, Laplace, Monge, Condorcet, and many other illustrious names in mathematics, physics, and astronomy; of A. L. de Jussieu, Lamarck, Cuvier, and Geoffroy Saint-Hilaire in botany, zoology, and paleontology; of Bichat in physiology and anatomy; and of Lavoisier, Berthollet, and the other French founders of modern chemistry.

What is difficult to comprehend—especially in view of the persistent tradition that the spirit of the Revolution was detrimental, if not actually antagonistic, to science—is that this scientific flowering was not fatally arrested or totally destroyed by the distractions of the Revolution, by the blood-bath of the Terror, by the mounting wave of emigration, or by the endless wars of the Republic, the Consulate, and the Empire. Yet this was clearly not the case. The scientific generation of the Napoleonic period and the Restoration—that of Arago, Poisson, Magendie, Gay-Lussac, Sadi Carnot, Cauchy, Fresnel, and the rest—is as rich if not richer in talent than the generations that came before. Yet we look in vain for truly comparable achievements in the art, the music, or the *belles lettres* of this revolutionary period; and we are forced to the conclusion that the national energy and the great social ferment that overthrew the Old Regime, spreading a new democratic gospel across Europe by flaming word and glinting bayonet, found its greatest cultural expression in scientific accomplishment.

Science and its practitioners played a notable role in the intellectual preparation for the Revolution as well as in the seething events of the Revolution itself. What this may have amounted to I can only summarize, in full realization of the complexity of the problem and the monographic work that remains to be done. My main purpose in this essay is to examine in preliminary fashion what happened to scientific progress, to scientific institutions, and to scientists themselves during the great Revolution, and to offer a general picture, tentative at best, that may help awaken the interest of other scholars in these problems and reveal, perhaps through my own errors, the gaps in our knowledge.

In the decade before the Revolution, European science felt the loss of such outstanding figures as Euler, Linnaeus, Daniel Bernouilli, and the great northern chemists, Scheele and Bergman. In France, d'Alembert died in 1783 and Buffon in 1788. Despite these losses, this was throughout Europe a time of extraordinary productivity and promise in the world of science, with France and England unquestionably in the lead, but with Switzerland, Italy, the German states, and Scandinavia boasting many proud names. As if to put the seal on France's acknowledged leadership, the eminent mathematician Lagrange, a native of Turin who for 20 years had been the beacon light of the Prussian Academy, left Berlin in 1787 after the death of Frederick the Great and took up his residence in Paris. It was here that he published in the following year his great *Mécanique analytique* under the auspices of the Royal Academy of Sciences. In 1789, the year of Revolution, there appeared three of the acknowledged classics of French science: A. L. de Jussieu's *Genera plantarum;* Philippe Pinel's *Nosographie philosophique;* and Lavoisier's epoch-making *Traité élémentaire de chimie.* Each work in its own domain—botany, medicine, and chemistry—was both a fulfillment and a new departure.

The swiftly moving events of the Revolution's first phase —the convening of the Estates General, the disorders in Paris and the provinces, the abolition of inherited privilege, the creation of a constitutional monarchy—found the scientists neither aloof nor unprepared. Having taken an active part in the liberal movement of the previous decades, they welcomed the first phase of the Revolution with enthusiasm; indeed, men like Bailly, Condorcet, and Lavoisier had played their modest part in bringing it about. Politics already infringed upon science, disturbing the tranquility of the laboratory and penetrating the fastnesses of the Academy of Sciences. On 4 July 1789 the Academicians took the unprecedented step of expressing to their fellow-member, the astronomer Bailly, their satisfaction at the manner in which he had performed his duties as president of the National Assembly; and later in the month the members of the Academy went in a body to Bailly's residence in Chaillot to pay their respects to him. Yet on the day following the storming of the Bastille the Academy held its regular meeting with 23 members present; technical papers were presented, and there is no echo in the *procès-verbaux* of the storm raging without (*1*). Throughout the remainder of 1789 and well into 1790, fundamental scientific questions continued to dominate the meetings of the Academy (*1*). Laplace read a series of important papers on celestial mechanics; Coulomb presented his sixth memoir on electrostatic experiments with the torsion balance; Lavoisier and Segum reported on their classic experiments on respiration and heat regulation in man and other animals, the last work on pure science carried out by the senior partner (*2*). There was great interest in current English work in observational astronomy; money was even set aside to build a great reflecting telescope, modeled upon the instrument with which the great English astronomer, William Herschel, was busy charting the nebulae and observing the rings and satellites of Saturn (*3*).

But concern about the effect of the revolutionary tensions and of the obsession with political events is reflected in the correspondence of the scientists. In August 1789 the chemist Berthollet wrote to James Watt (4):

> While you are occupied tranquilly with science and the useful arts which owe you such great obligations, we have been obliged to lose sight of them. The ferocity of the great nobles, the insurrection of the citizens, the fury of the people, the scourge of famine have absorbed all our attention; yet one must return to peaceful occupations, and one can begin to enjoy the pleasures of study. I am taking up my experiments once more.

And the mathematician Gaspard Monge, toward the end of the same year, commented to the same correspondent (5):

> Our Revolution occupies every mind, each in his own fashion; and science is the loser. May God bring it to a swift conclusion, for we shall lose the habit of work and the love of science.

Lavoisier wrote in like vein to the Scottish chemist, Joseph Black, lamenting the interruption of scientifc activity and expressing the hope that calm and prosperity would soon allow the scientists to return to their laboratories (6). While from Chaptal, the founder of French industrial chemistry, we have the following cautious appraisals of the opportunities and dangers that lay ahead (7):

> The revolution which is taking place is a beautiful thing, but I wish it had arrived twenty years ago. It is annoying to find oneself under a house that is being torn down, but that is precisely our position. . . . In this general confusion, in this torrent of passions, the intelligent man studies the role he should play: but it seems just as dangerous to remain outside of the excitement as to participate.

As these letters indicate, the scientists were being inexorably drawn into the revolutionary turmoil. In 1788 Lavoisier had prepared a long memorandum on the proper constitution of the Estates General; early in 1789 he took a major part in drawing up the *cahier* of grievances to instruct the representatives of the nobility of Blois; and in May he was chosen alternate deputy to the Estates General. The astronomer Bailly was one of the political leaders of the first Revolutionary assembly; and shortly afterward was chosen the first mayor of Paris. The mathematician Condorcet, Perpetual Secretary of the Academy of Science, plunged at once into the journalistic and political activity that led to his election—along with such other scientists as Tenon, Lacépède, Fourcroy, and Guyton de Morveau—to one or another of the succeeding assemblies. Other scientists were active in the Paris *sections,* or Revolutionary districts, and served in battalions of the National Guard.

By the time of the acceptance of the constitution in September 1791, the moderates—and they included all but a handful of the younger scientists—hoped, as we have just seen, that the violent and disruptive phase of the Revolution was at an end and that the time had come to plan constructively for the future. To this end there was founded in April of 1790 a short-lived but influential association called the Society of 1789, which aspired to be the intellectual guide and official planning agency of the new society and its elected assembly. Besides well-known liberals and reformers of the pre-Revolutionary period—Brissot, Dupont de Nemours, Mirabeau, Talleyrand—it included influential members of the Academy of Sciences: Condorcet and Lavoisier; the mathematician Gaspard Monge; the biologist Lacépède and Lamarck, and others (8). Briefly, from June through September 1790, this society published a journal, edited by Condorcet, which is our only direct evidence of what transpired in their meetings and of the philosophy that pervaded them. The society's avowed purpose (9) was to aid and promote

. . . all discoveries useful to the progress of *l'art social,* to encourage those being made in these sciences themselves and to gather together suggestions relative to public institutions that may be formed for public welfare and for education.

A perusal of this short-lived journal shows that, besides treating in rather high-flown and abstract language such basic social problems as the rights of women and the proper foreign policy for a free nation, it devoted space to the discussion of the national economy and the importance of a scientific technology (10). Lavoisier read a famous paper on the *assignats* and the inflationary dangers of a paper currency. The chemist Hassenfratz wrote on the importance of promoting the useful arts; contributed a long article on the mineral resources of France and the possibilities of developing them; and described in another number recent advances in chemical industry: LeBlanc's famous soda process and Berthrollet's use of hypochlorites for bleaching.

In the discussions of this society are to be found, I believe, the germs of many of the constructive revolutionary accomplishments: the various efforts undertaken to stimulate productive industry and invention; possibly also the great reform in weights and measures and the creation of the metric system, although this had earlier antecedents; but above all, although direct evidence is lacking in the *Journal*, the plans for new educational and scientific institutions, such as those later elaborated by Talleyrand and Condorcet.

The philosophy of science, or rather of social science, that guided these men is worthy of a moment's attention. It centers upon Condorcet's conception of a unified social science, an *art social,* based upon a collaboration and unification of the sciences according to a common spirit and, where possible, a common methodology. The vision of what Comte was to call *sociology* is clearly discernible in the manifesto of the society drawn up by Condorcet (*11*):

There should exist for all societies a science of maintaining and extending their happiness: this is what has been called *l'art social.* This science, to which all others are contributors, has not been treated as a whole. The science of agriculture, the science of economics, the science of government . . . are only portions of this greater science. These separate sciences will not reach their complete development until they have been made into a well-organized whole. . . . And this result will be obtained sooner if all the workers are led to follow a constant and uniform method of work.

If one asked of Condorcet how such a unification of the sciences could be brought about, how the experimental and mathematical spirit of the natural sciences could be transferred to the sciences of man and society, he would not have agreed with the early system-builders of the 18th century, or with John Stuart Mill, that it is enough to build aprioristic deductive systems in imitation of the great scheme of classical mechanics. Condorcet placed his faith in what he called social mathematics, embodying the twin disciplines of social statistics and mathematical probability, subjects to which he had contributed, together with Laplace and Lavoisier, in the years before the Revolution. Just at this time he was preparing a popular exposition of social mathematics in his *Elémens du calcul des probabilités,* for he saw in it a useful instrument of social improvement and reform. In his preface he explains why he feels that social mathematics was at this moment indispensable; and he continues (*12*):

> When a Revolution has ended, this method of treating the social sciences takes a new direction and acquires a greater degree of utility. In fact, to repair promptly the dislocations inseparable from every great movement, to restore general prosperity, one needs stronger methods [than mere argument], means calculated with greater precision, supported by unattackable proofs in order to ensure the adoption of needed reforms in the face of selfish interests and base faith.

We hardly need to remind ourselves that when Condorcet wrote, the Revolution had not ended but was moving with torrential rapidity toward greater confusions and dangers, in which science and scientists alike suffered. Later men like Quetelet, Cournot, and Auguste Comte in the nineteenth century were to pick up, each in his own fashion, the prophetic program that Condorcet was obliged to abandon.

Even before the outbreak of war in 1792, the demands of a succession of revolutionary governments upon the Academy of Sciences and its members left little time for normal activities. By all odds the most time-consuming and exacting responsibility—overshadowing such requests as that the Academy examine and test silver vessels taken from *ci-devant* churches and recommend the proper method of reconverting the secularized church bells of bronze and bell-metal—was the great project for the standardization and rationalization of the system of weights and measures. By a decree of 8 May 1790 the National Assembly charged the Academy of Sciences with determining the best scheme, based upon some universal standard found in nature, that might be adopted by all nations. Early in 1791 the Academy recommended a decimal system of units, derived from a unit of length, the meter, to be established by geodetic measurements. After a favorable report by Talleyrand to the Assembly, the Academy was assigned the task of making the basic measurements and preparing a reliable set of primary standards. This involved a long and tedious series of operations, still not completed when the Academy was abolished in August 1793.

Despite this drain on its personnel and energy, the Academy continued regular sessions until the summer of 1793. Even in the final six months of its existence, regular meetings were still being held, although the exigencies of national defense and the mobilization of science for war—one of the earliest such phenomena in history—sometimes reduced the participants to a mere handful. The Academy even continued its practice of announcing the subjects of annual prize contests (*13*). A subject proposed for the year 1793 is of special interest. The prize was to be awarded for the best theoretical analysis of the operation of steam engines, with a discussion of methods for their improvement (*14*), surely one of the most important technical problems of the time. No prize was actually awarded, although it was again announced in 1793 for the year 1795, no memoirs having been received, and the problem was finally attacked for the first time a generation later by Sadi Carnot, the son of the man who in these years was organizing the victory of the Republican armies.

During this crucial period the collapse and destruction of many of the venerable scientific institutions had an equally damaging effect upon the progress of science. The *Imprimerie Nationale,* now flooded with job-printing for the government, could no longer serve, as it had throughout the eighteenth century, for the publication of scientific books. Important serial publications, among them the *Journal des savants,* the *Mémoires* of the Academy of Sciences, and even the newly founded *Annales de chimie,* were suspended because of lack of funds or contributors. But the most serious blow was the suppression, in August 1793, of the venerable Academy of Sciences.

The detailed story of the Academy's fall has yet to be written, and I shall not attempt it here. Its ultimate fate, and that of the other royal academies, was heatedly debated from 1790 to 1793. While the monarchy lasted, eloquent voices were raised to preserve it virtually unchanged, but vitriolic attacks had already begun, both within and without the assemblies, demanding its immediate abolition as an aristocratic remnant of the past, and as a "school of servility and falsehood." Effective pamphleteers, chief among them J. P. Marat, attacked the Academy and its members unmercifully in the public press. As far as I have been able to judge, the plan most widely favored—for example, by men like Talleyrand and Condorcet—was to effect a peaceable transformation of academies, including the Academy of Sciences, into learned bodies more acceptable to the new climate of opinion; until this could be effected it was hoped to continue the Academy virtually unchanged. These tactics were very nearly successful, as they proved to be in the case of the Jardin du Roi, which emerged enlarged and strengthened as the Muséum d'Histoire Naturelle, a research center of great importance. Disagreement within the Academy of Sciences brought delay, and delay was fatal. While defending the academies before the Legislative Assembly in 1791, the Abbé Grégoire made known that the academies were, of their own accord, reforming their statutes to put them in harmony with the new era and erasing traces of their monarchical past. There is evidence that such a draft of new statutes was actually prepared by the Academy of Sciences, but it seems to have been without effect (15).

On 8 August 1793, Grégoire read to the Convention a report on behalf of the Committee of Public Instruction in which he proposed the suppression of the academies, in order to reorganize these bodies, as he put it, in the light of human wisdom and progress. The Academy of Sciences alone, by virtue of its special utility, was to escape suppression. But the Convention was in no mood to brook exceptions; after a vituperative speech by the painter Louis David, the Academy of Sciences was extinguished with the others. The members were even denied the privilege of constituting themselves a Free Scientific Society and of using their accustomed meeting place in the Louvre. The doors were closed and sealed; soon after, these echoing chambers were invaded by an army of tailors, busy stitching uniforms for the Revolutionary armies, while workers removed the last vestiges of monarchical symbolism from the walls.

Several years were to elapse before the constructive plans of the Convention replaced or successfully remodeled the older scientific institutions. Under the Directory, harried as it was by inflation and war, there nevertheless were miraculously established those scientific institutions which were to be the boast and pride of France during the succeeding century: the Institut de France, the Ecole Polytechnique, the Conservatoire des Arts et Metiers, the brilliant but ephemeral Ecole Normale, the Muséum d'Histoire Naturelle. The result of prolonged planning and debate, going back at least to the discussions in the Society of 1789 and in the early Revolutionary assemblies, the final formulation of these plans must be credited to the Convention, the most ruthless and determined of the Revolutionary governments. This fact was conveniently forgotten by the writers and propagandists of Napoleonic days, who left the impression that Bonaparte, almost singlehanded, had saved French science, which the Jacobins had sought to destroy.

Soon after the collapse of the Academy, organized scientific work came to a virtual standstill. Under the Jacobins' iron rule, the Republican Conservatives—the Girondist opposition—were herded to public execution in the Place de la Révolution. The astronomer Bailly joined Philippe Egalité, Mme. Roland, and lesser enemies of Robespierre in the tumbrils of the guillotine. The members of the General Farm, the tax-collecting corporation of the Old Régime, were arrested in the fall of 1793, the chemist Lavoisier among them. Tried before the Revolutionary Tribunal on 8 May 1794 and convicted of a specious charge of conspiring with the enemies of the Republic, all were executed on the same day. The scientific community stood in appalled confusion. Many, like Laplace, found hiding places in the country (it was in such circumstances, for example, that he completed his popular *Système du monde*). Trapped on the outskirts of Paris, Condorcet is said to have taken his own life with poison foresightedly obtained from his friend Cabanis, the physician and philosopher (*16*). Yet it is astonishing to record that no scientist of note joined the flood of emigrés, which reached its peak in these years. Against none of the scientists, moreover, can a charge of counter-revolutionary activity be seriously maintained. On the other hand, few of Lavoisier's erstwhile coworkers—not Fourcroy, Guyton-Morveau, Monge, or Berthollet, all of whom were serving the Convention—raised a voice in his defense, nor had they openly protested the arrest of Bailly. Political passion, fear, and perhaps personal resentments may explain, but cannot condone, this conduct.

After 9 Thermidor (27 July 1794) when Robespierre fell, sanity returned and the scientists could survey the wreckage. The vandalism toward the scientific institutions, the execution of Bailly and Lavoisier, were at once held up as among the most abominable of Robespierre's crimes. Condorcet was accorded his apotheosis as patron saint of a new learned publication, the *Décade philosophique* founded in 1794, organ of the so-called "Idéologues." In Millin's *Magasin encyclopédique* there appeared, the year following the execution of the Farmers General, the first biographical sketch of Lavoisier, a factual but moving account by his long-time friend, the astronomer Lalande (*17*). The same year a somewhat nauseating memorial service was held for Lavoisier at the Lycée des Arts, the main feature of which was a ponderous eulogy by Fourcroy, the erstwhile Jacobin, who sought to defend his failure to aid Lavoisier (*18*).

It is of some interest that even during these critical years, and before the creation of the new scientific institutions, a thin but persistent thread of scientific activity is clearly evident. Private initiative took over where the public institutions gave way or were destroyed. The old Lycée de Paris, a center for public lectures founded in 1789, took on considerable importance until it was shunned for harboring men suspected of antirevolutionary proclivities. Its more scientific and utilitarian competitor, the Lycée des Arts, was founded in 1792 and flourished through the darkest days of the Terror. It stressed the application of science to the useful arts, and among its outstanding lecturers were Fourcroy, Berthollet, Daubenton, and Jussieu (*19*). Millin's *Magasin encyclopédique,* begun in 1792 but not firmly established until 1795, gives a picture of its activities and was in some respect its organ.

Of more importance for fundamental scientific work were two new societies whose rebirth, in one case, and prosperity, in the other, were due to the conditions I have described. The first of these, the Société d'Histoire Naturelle, had been founded, only to disband, in 1788. It was revived after the Revolution, and an English commentator wrote of it as follows in 1793 (*20*):

. . . the disadvantages to which it was exposed, in common with the non-privileged societies, under the old government, and the jealousy of some of the protected literary bodies [i.e. the Academies] soon caused its dissolution.

After the revolution, its founders, however, reunited, extended their plan, and instituted the present Society of Natural History, which was joined by all the naturalists of the capital.

. . . The object of their labours is Natural History in general, but especially that of France, and in particular of the environs of Paris. . . . New researches are to be made by means of periodical excursions taken by the Society, either in the country, at the proper seasons of the year, or to gardens, museums, etc. . . .

This is rather too peaceful and bucolic a picture for this period of general harassment, but it is certain that the society became genuinely active after Thermidor. It was frequented by the professors of the Muséum d'Histoire Naturelle, which had early made its peace with the Revolution and where substantial scientific work was being accomplished by men like Lacépède, Lamarck, and Cuvier. Significant papers by these men and others were published in the society's *Journal,* which appeared briefly in 1792, and in its *Mémoires,* first published in 1799 (*21*).

A second and distinctly more important scientific society owed its inception, like the Natural History Society, to the fact that it was no longer necessary to obtain royal approval (and, in addition, at least the passive acquiescence of the Academy of Sciences) for a society holding scientific meetings and issuing a regular publication. This was the Société Philomathique, which played a very useful role in the scientific life of this troubled period and has continued to this day. Beginning in 1788 as an informal discussion group of six almost unknown physicians and scientific amateurs, it was joined, in September 1789, by the young chemist Vauquelin and a few others. These men constituted themselves as a regularly organized scientific society, with dues, correspondents, and the project of publishing a monthly *Bulletin* or journal. Its membership increased slowly between 1790 and 1792, but as yet it attracted no important scientists. But suddenly, after the suppression of the Academy of Sciences, distinguished names were added to the roster. In 1793 the Société Philomathique was joined by Berthollet, Fourcroy, Monge, Lamarck, and Lavoisier, that is to say, by the acknowledged luminaries of the *ci-devant* Academy of Sciences. Between the time the Academy was abolished in August 1793 and the autumn of 1796, when the Institut de France was formally established, the Société Philomathique was the principal haven of the dispossessed scientists. It maintained close ties with the Société d'Histoire Naturelle, and with the scientists at the Museum. After Thermidor, its president referred to it as the only society officially recognized as having offered during the period of terrorism "un point fixe de réunion aux sciences et aux arts" (22).

In 1791 its *Bulletin* was launched as a monthly summary of scientific progress that was circulated in manuscript among the members. In 1792 it was printed in a few copies but consisted only of short abstracts. Its first real issue as a learned journal is that of April 1797. The printer, of whom we must say a few words, was the economist and publicist, Dupont de Nemours, erstwhile member of the Society of 1789 and close friend of many scientists.

Private initiative once again filled the gap left by the loss to the Academy of Sciences of the facilities of the Imprimerie Nationale, which during the eighteenth century had printed the official publications of the Academy, and many individual works of science bearing the seal of its approval. Private printers like the Jomberts and the Didots had made something of a specialty of scientific printing during the eighteenth century, and they were by no means inactive during the Revolution. But the man who should be notable for coming to the aid of the scientists in this capacity during the period of crisis is Dupont de Nemours. In June 1791, he was leaving the Constituent Assembly, Dupont issued a prospectus informing the public that he was opening a well-equipped publishing house where, he said, he proposed to do "good and inexpensive work for those who are chiefly interested in the contents of a book" (23). This venture of Dupont's is well known, but it is usually assumed that he printed only political tracts and his *Correspondence patriotique*. Nor is it widely known that the Lavoisiers, husband and wife, were among his sponsors (24). From then Dupont borrowed the sum of 710,000 francs for the purchase of his printing house. It is therefore not surprising to find that Dupont had a share in publishing works of his earlier associates in the Society of 1789. In 1791 he helped bring out Talleyrand's famous report on public education and printed Lavoiser's *Etat des finances de France*. In 1793 he published the *Réflexions sur l'instruction publique,* which Lavoisier drafted in the name of the Bureau de consultation des arts et métiers.

A number of scientific books also appeared over Dupont's imprint: the first edition of Fourcroy's *Philosophie chimique* (1792) and a second edition in 1795; a treatise by Antoine Portal on tuberculosis (1792); two editions of Daubenton's

Tableau méthodique des minéraux; a *Flora* of the Pyrenees by Picot de la Peyrouse (1795), and other works. Dupont was the official printer for the Academy of Sciences from 1791 until its dissolution (he is so listed in the *Almanach Royal*), and in this capacity did such job-printing as the prize announcement of the Academy mentioned in the preceding section. In 1794 Dupont published the belated volume of the *Mémoires* of the Academy for 1789 and, in 1797, the volume for 1790. He was also, as we have learned, publisher of the *Bulletin* of the Société Philomathique *(25)*.

Some general remarks about the character of scientific work in this period seem appropriate here. If we cite at random, as I did at the beginning of this article, the great names that illuminated these decades, we convey the impression of distinguished and virtually uninterrupted scientific progress. A closer examination does not confirm this. The first years of the Revolution, perhaps to 1792, were still quite productive, because the momentum of the previous years was not immediately arrested. The really creative period of the men of the Revolutionary generation—men who, like Lagrange, Lavoisier, Monge, Berthollet, and Laplace, were in their forties or early fifties in 1789—falls in the years before the Revolution. Monge presented in his lectures at the Ecole Normale his great invention of descriptive geometry, but this had been worked out long before when he taught at the Ecole de Mézières. The monumental *Mécanique celeste* of Laplace did not begin to appear until 1799, but the work seems to have been well advanced by 1790 and, but for the Revolution, might have been completed much sooner. The same rule seems to hold for Legendre's *Essay on the Theory of Numbers* (1794) and his work on elliptic functions (1798), both of which grew out of earlier work.

Those scientists of the older generation who survived the turmoil of the Revolution—and they were the great majority—made their greatest contributions in this period as inspiring teachers of the Napoleonic generation. Indeed the production of brilliant pedagogic works is a marked feature of the period from 1794 to 1800. Monge's lectures are in this category, and so were the later books of Lagrange, based on his teaching at the Ecole Normale and the Ecole Polytechnique. Laplace's famous *Essai philosophique sur les probabilités* grew out of lectures delivered at the Ecole Normale in 1795. An outstandingly successful example is Legendre's *Eléments de géométrie,* a skillful reworking of Euclid. And on a lower plane were the immensely popular mathematical textbooks of Sylvestre Lacroix, widely used at one time in this country. Laplace's readable *Exposition du système du monde,* like his general discussion of probability just mentioned, was clearly a manifestation of a desire to present serious scientific speculation to a wide audience, yet in a spirit markedly different from the glib popularizations of the eighteenth century.

A similar phenomenon is observed in chemistry, where the great textbooks of Chaptal and Fourcroy, and the latter's *Dictionary of Chemistry* in the *Encyclopédie méthodique,* sought to present in intelligent order the facts of the new chemistry. The pioneer works on applied chemistry by Chaptal and Berthollet emphasize another aspect of this new orientation.

The naturalists of the Muséum, chief among them Lamarck, form something of a special case. Sustained, even pampered, by the Revolutionaries of the Left, the workers at the Muséum were less adversely affected by events. It was the revolutionists who called Lamarck, a man of fifty and a botanist, to the newly created chair of invertebrate zoology; and here during the subsequent years he did his best and most famous work, developing his theory of biological evolution and collecting the materials for his pioneer descriptive treatise of invertebrate zoology (1815–1822).

That science lost much that the Revolutionary generation intended to accomplish is suggested by what we know of the work of leading Academicians on the eve of the Terror. Had the great reflecting telescope been built, it might have turned French astronomy into channels of observational astronomy in which, in the nineteenth century, other countries, including America, surpassed her. But the money set aside for this purpose was presented to the Convention as a *don patriotique* in a frantic effort of ingratiation.

From what we have recently learned of the plans and projects of Lavoisier at the time he was lost to science, we see that his creative energies had in no sense flagged. He was forty-six when the Revolution broke out, and if he could have matured his scientific plans uninterruptedly the results might have been incalculable. At the time of his imprison-

ment he was preparing a fundamental revision of his *Traité
élémentaire de chimie* and an edition of his collected works;
and only recently it has been pointed out that in addition he
had outlined a great work of chemical theory, or, as he said,
of *philosophie chimique* (26). More important still, he considered his last work on respiration and body heat control as
a starting point for a research program in what we would
now call medical biochemistry. A passage in Lalande's
sketch of Lavoisier, which has been generally overlooked,
makes this point with pardonable exaggeration (27):

By these curious and difficult experiments [on body chem-
istry] he had already acquired insight into the causes of different
diseases and on ways of supplementing nature in their cure, and
he was preparing to attack the reversed and ancient colossus of
medical prejudice and error. Nothing was more important than
this work of Lavoisier; and one can say that if the sciences have
experienced an irreparable loss, all humanity should join us in
lamenting this privation.

Except for Bichat and some of the younger naturalists I
have mentioned, the men who were between the ages of
eighteen and thirty in 1789 belonged to a lost generation:
men old enough to have their earliest productive years
blighted by the storm, too old to benefit by the great schools
and the illustrious masters that prepared the Napoleonic
generation. Yet the brilliance and the diversity of talent that
blossomed in the first decades of the nineteenth century tes-
tify to the fundamental vitality of science in Revolutionary
France. Clearly there were shifts of emphasis toward a
broader democratic base of scientific instruction, toward a
greater preoccupation of scientists with problems of industrial application and questions of social utility. Those men
of science, a small though illustrious minority, who lost their
lives during the Terror, were men who had, to a large extent,
given up science for politics. It was as politicians, financiers,
and public officials that they were executed, not as men of
science. Although the Revolution, as any such painful crisis
must, produced profound dislocations, it yielded also en-
during benefits in industrial progress and new scientific institutions. At no point can we simply affirm, as did the men who
wished to blacken still further the men of the Revolution,
that the Revolution felt it had no need of men of science.

NOTES

1. *Procès-Verbaux de l'Académie Royale des Sciences*, Année, 1789, T. 108; Annés 1790–93, T. 109; in *Archives de l'Académie des Sciences*.
2. *Oeuvres de Lavoisier*, vol. II, pp. 688–714.
3. J. Lalande, "Histoire de l'astronomie, pour 1792," in *Connaissance des Tems pour l'année sextile VIIᵉ de la République* (Paris, 1797), p. 236.
4. J. P. Muirhead, *Mechanical Inventions of James Watt* (London, 1844), vol. II, p. 228.
5. Letter of 10 Dec. 1789, in Muirhead, *op. cit.*, vol. II. p. 237.
6. Letter of 5 July 1790 cited by E. Grimaux, *Lavoisier* (Paris, ed. 2, 1896), pp. 201–202.
7. J. Pigeire, *La vie et l'oeuvre de Chaptal* (Paris, 1932), p. 124.
8. A. Challamel, *Les clubs contre-révolutionnaires* (Paris, 1885), pp. 390–443. See also Condorcet, "A Monsieur xxx, sur la société de 1789," *Oeuvres de Condorcet*, vol. X, p. 69, where we learn that an informal nucleus of this society had been in existence since Oct. 1789.
9. "Règlemens de la Société de 1789 et liste des membres," in Challamel, *op. cit.*, p. 393.
10. The Andrew D. White Collection of books and pamphlets on the French Revolution at Cornell University has a bound volume of the 15 numbers of the *Journal de la Société de 1789*, from 5 June to 15 Sept. 1790, together with the prospectus of the *Journal*.
11. Challamel, *op. cit.*, p. 393. See also M. J. Laboulle, "La mathématique sociale: Condorcet et ses prédécesseurs," *Revue d'histoire littéraire de la France* **46**, 33 (1939).
12. Condorcet, *Elémens du calcul des probabilités, et son application aux jeux de hazard, à la lotterie, et aux jugements des hommes, par Feu M. de Condorcet, Avec un discours sur les avantages des mathématiques sociales et une notice sur M. de Condorcet* (Paris, An XIII—1805).
13. A "prix national d'utilité" had been awarded in 1791 to the English astronomer William Herschel and in 1792 to Paul Mascagni (1752–1815) for his magnificent illustrated work on the lymphatics. See Lalande, "Histoire de l'astronomie, pour 1792," *loc. cit.*, p. 249.
14. This prize of 1080 livres, the Prix Montyon, for the best memoir tending to simplify the processes of some mechanical art had been awarded in 1792 to a M. Girard, an engineer of Poitiers, for his study of the best method of constructing locks for canals and harbors. See *Prix Proposé par l'Académie Royale des Sciences, Pour l'année 1793*, 2 pp., de l'Imprimerie de Dupont, Imprimeur de l'Académie des Sciences, 1792 (Collection de Chazelles, Bibliothèque de Clermont-Ferrand).

15. When this paper was delivered, the existence of these new statutes was a mere surmise. After a search in the records of the *Académie des Sciences,* in the summer of 1954, two working copies were discovered. These regulations were debated for nearly 6 months and were finally approved by the Academy on 13 Sept. 1790; they were never officially promulgated or printed.

16. It is more likely that Condorcet died of a circulatory disorder brought about by fatigue, exposure, and hunger. See J. S. Schapiro, *Condorcet* (New York, 1934), pp. 106–107.

17. *Magasin encyclopédique* 5, 174 (1795).

18. *Notice sur la vie et les travaux de Lavoisier, précédée d'un discours sur les funérailles, et suivie d'une ode sur l'immortalité de l'Ame* (Paris, L'An Quatrième, 1795).

19. Ch. Dejob, *De l'établissement connu sous le nom de Lycée et d'Athénée et de quelques établissements analogues* (Paris, 1889).

20. "A discourse on the origin and progress of natural history in France," *Memoirs of Science & the Arts, etc.* (London, 1793), vol. I, pt. II, p. 448. On the early days of the society, see C. G. Krafft, *Notice sur Aubin-Louis Millin* (Paris, 1818), pp. 8–10.

21. *Mémoires de la Société d'histoire naturelle de Paris* (Paris, Prairial An VII, 1799), see especially pp. iii–ix. The activities of this society can be followed in the *Magasin encyclopédique* from 1795 onward.

22. Marcellin Berthelot, "Origines et histoire de la société philomathique," *Mémoires publiées par la Société philomathique à l'occasion du centenaire de sa fondation, 1788–1888* (Paris, 1888), pp. i–xv. For the constituent articles and the list of early members, see the *Rapports généraux des travaux de la Société philomathique de Paris* (Paris, n.d., 1800?).

23. See his prospectus entitled *Imprimerie de Dupont Député de Nemours à l'Assemblée Nationale,* dated 8 June, 1791 (*Bib. Nat.* Vp 21199). An English version of this document is published in B. E. du Pont, *Life of Eleuthère Irenée du Pont from Contemporary Correspondence* (Newark, Del., 1923), vol. I, pp. 141–145.

24. See B. E. du Pont, *op. cit.,* vol. I, p. 185, note 1.

25. Dupont's undated *Notice sur l'institution de la Société philomathique,* an 8-page pamphlet, probably dated from the period of the society's rapid expansion, 1792 or 1793. A copy of this was found among the Lavoisier papers (dossier 162) in the *Archives de l'Académie des sciences.*

26. M. Dumas, "L'élaboration du Traité de chimie de Lavoisier," *Archives Internationales d'Histoire des Sciences* (1950, vol. XXIX, pp. 570–590).

27. *Magasin encyclopédique* 5, 183 (1795).

Influence of Philosophic Trends on the

Formulation of Scientific Theories

ACCORDING to Philipp Frank [*Sci. Monthly* **79**, 139 (1954)], the reasons for, or against, the acceptance of certain scientific theories are not always restricted to the *technical value* of the theory in question—that is, to its ability to give us a consistent explanation of the phenomena it is dealing with; instead, these reasons involve a series of other factors.

Thus, in the case of Copernican astronomy, the choice was not merely one between a more simple and a more complicated theory of celestial motions, but also a choice between a more simple and a seemingly more complicated physics, between—as Bacon very aptly pointed out—reliance on, or rejection of, sense perception as a basis of physical knowledge, and so forth.

I am in perfect agreement with Frank. I only fear that he did not go far enough, and that, in his analysis, he made a rather unfortunate omission, namely, that of the philosophic background of the conflicting theories. It is, indeed, my contention that the role of this "philosophic background" has always been of utmost importance, and that, in history, the influence of philosophy upon science has been as important as the influence—which everybody admits—of science upon philosophy. As an example illustrating my assertion I would like to consider the period of post-Copernican science, the period commonly considered to be that of the *origin of modern science,* I mean the science that dominated our thinking for about three centuries, roughly speaking, from Galileo to Einstein and Planck.

Everybody agrees that the seventeenth century accomplished or underwent a deep cultural, philosophic, scientific revolution. From our point of view, and for our purposes, this revolution can be characterized as (i) the destruction of the *cosmos,* that is, the substitution for the hierarchically structured finite world of the Aristotelian tradition of the infinite universe bound together by the uniformity of its fundamental components and laws; and (ii) the geometrization of space, that is, substitution for the concrete physically structured place-space of Aristotle of the abstract, isomorphous, and infinite dimension-space of Euclidean geometry now considered as real.

The cosmologic and physical conceptions of Aristotelian science, or natural philosophy, have—the existence of some orthodox Thomists notwithstanding—generally speaking a very bad reputation. Some of the moderns, especially philosophers and psychologists, go so far as to tax Aristotle's reasonings as infantile and attribute to him the mental age of a child of twelve.

Historians of science treat him scarcely better. This, in my opinion, is to be explained only by the continuity of the anti-Aristotelian tradition inherited from the founders of modern science who—and which—asserted themselves in a victorious struggle *against* Aristotle; and by the persistence of both the historiographic tradition of the nineteenth century and the value judgments of the first modern historians of science—an eighteenth and nineteenth century creation.

For these historians, born, bred, and reared in the Newtonian world, which—though with some rather important structural additions—has been accepted, not only as real and true, but even as conforming to the natural world-conception of the human mind, the very idea of a finite, closed cosmos appeared ludicrous. What ridicule, indeed, has not been piled upon Aristotle for his discussion of the dimensions of the world, or of its weight, or for holding that bodies could move naturally without being dragged or pushed from outside, for his belief that circular motion was a particularly interesting and important kind of motion, the very pattern of a natural one.

We know today—although, perhaps we have not yet quite *accepted* and *admitted* it—that all this is, perhaps, not quite so ridiculous as it seemed to be yesterday; and that Aristotle was much more right than he knew himself. As a matter of fact, circular motion *does* play a particularly important role in the world and is particularly well represented in it; so well that for a *natural* object it seems to be a *natural* thing to turn and rotate. Indeed, every thing does so: the galaxies and nebulae, the stars and the sun and the planets, and atoms and electrons; even photons seem to conform to the general rule.

The spontaneous motion of bodies, as we know full well since Einstein, is quite normal, provided that, of course, the space is conveniently curved; and we know, too, or at least believe we know, that our universe is by no means infinite (although it has no boundaries) and that "outside" this universe there is strictly nothing, just because there is no "outside" to the world, and all world-space is "inside."

Now this is precisely what—somewhat clumsily, because he did not have at his disposal the resources of Riemannian geometry—Aristotle has been teaching us. Outside the world, he said, there is *nothing,* pure nothing, neither *plenum* nor *vacuum,* neither place nor space, because all the space—that is, all the places where something can be—is *inside.*

The Aristotelian conception is, of course, not mathematical; this is its weakness, but also its strength. It is a metaphysical one. The world of Aristotle is not a mathematically curved world; it is, so to speak, a metaphysically curved world.

Contemporary cosmologists, when they try to explain to us the structure of the Einsteinian, or post-Einsteinian, curved space and finite though boundless universe, are wont to point out that they are dealing with difficult mathematical conceptions, and that those of us who are not sufficiently trained and who lack ability in mathematical thinking will not be able fully to understand them. They are perfectly right, of course. Yet it is perhaps interesting to note that they are only repeating, indeed, turning upside down, what medieval philosophers, when they were dealing with Aristotelian cosmology, explained to their readers; thus they (Henricus of Ghent, for instance, in the late thirteenth century) did not fail to point out that they were using difficult metaphysical reasonings and concepts, and that those who were not sufficiently trained in, or gifted for, metaphysical thinking and who could not rise above the level of geometric imagining, could not understand Aristotle; they would continue to ask: What is outside the world? What will happen if we push a stick through the surface of the ultimate heavenly sphere?

The real difficulty of the Aristotelian conception—solved ultimately by Riemann and Einstein—consists, obviously, in the necessity of providing a place for Euclidean geometry inside the world. Yet, for Aristotle, it was by no means a decisive difficulty, for, in the Aristotelian conception, geometry is not a fundamental science that discloses the necessary structure of physical being but only an abstract and subservient one. Experience, sense perception, not *a priori* mathematical reasoning, are for him the true bases of physics, the science that deals with nature and gives us knowledge of the real world.

On the other hand, for Plato, who believed in mathematics and did *not* believe in sense perception, and who had tried to link together the idea of a cosmos and an attempt to construct the physical world, the world of matter and of change, out of pure geometric space ($\chi\tilde{\omega}\rho\alpha$), the situation was, of course, much more difficult. It had to be one or the other. The choice, sooner or later, had to be made. It was unavoidable, although about 2000 years passed before it was made in fact, and it was just this acceptance of the complete geometrization of space and, consequently, the rejection of the cosmos that characterized the Platonism of the seventeenth century, that of Galileo and of Descartes, and in this sense opposed it to the world-view of Plato himself.

It seems to me rather obvious that the revolution of the seventeenth century, which substituted for the qualitative world of sense perception and everyday life the Archimedean world of geometry made real, cannot be explained simply by the influence, or effect, of an enlarged or enriched experience (sense experience).

1) As P. Tannery and P. Duhem have already shown, Aristotelian science (physics), precisely because it was based on sense perception and common-sense experience and thus was really and truly *empirical,* was in much better accord with perception and experience than the new science of mathematical dynamics.

After all, bodies really fall when they are *heavy* and rise when they are *light;* and the principle of inertia, according to which bodies when pushed or thrown continue their motion indefinitely in a straight line, is certainly not based on experience, which constantly disproves this principle. Inertial motion, indeed, not only has never been encountered in the world, but it is even impossible that it ever should be.

2) The infinity of the universe cannot, of course, be asserted on the ground of experience. The infinite, as Aristotle had pointed out, cannot be traversed or given; compared

with eternity a billion years is as nothing, and the world revealed by the Palomar reflector is by no means greater than that of the Greeks. Yet the infinity of the universe is an essential element of the axiomatic structure of modern science and is implied by its fundamental laws, as Euler and Einstein have both recognized.

3) The experiences alleged by the promoters of the new science, or their historians, prove nothing whatever, because (i) such as they were actually made they are nothing less than precise, (ii) in order to serve as proof they would require an extrapolation to infinity, and (iii) they have, allegedly, to demonstrate to us the existence of something—inertial motion—that is strictly and rigorously impossible.

The validity of these experiences presupposes the mathematical structure of nature, the mathematical language of (physical) science.

The birth of modern science is concomitant with a transformation (we could even call it mutation) of the axiomatic framework of human thoughts, with a shift in the evaluation of intellectual knowledge as compared with the knowledge given to us by sense perception, and with the discovery that —as Descartes suggested—the idea of the infinite is a clear and positive idea, in spite of its being (falsely) expressed by a negative term, and that it is *therefore* a true one—that is, an idea which gives us access to the real world.

Thus it is perfectly fitting that this infinitization of the universe (the breaking of the circle, as Marjorie Nicolson has called it, or the bursting of the sphere, as I prefer to call it) should have been announced by a philosopher—Giordano Bruno—and opposed for scientific and empirical reasons by the great astronomer Kepler.

Giordano Bruno is neither a very great philosopher nor a very good scientist, and the reasons he gives in favor of the infinity of the universe and the intellectual primacy of the infinite are not particularly clear. Giordano Bruno is not Descartes. Yet we know that not only in philosophy but even in pure science—take, for instance, the case of Kepler, or that of Dalton, or even that of Maxwell—faulty reasoning from inexact premises sometimes leads to perfectly sound and even extremely important results.

Fifteen years ago, I called the revolution of the 17th century "la revanche de Platon." But, as a matter of fact, it was an alliance, an alliance with Democritus, that decided the old strife and enabled Plato to defeat Aristotle.

Strange alliance! Yet we know that not only in the history of philosophy or ideas but also in history *tout court* these strange alliances of seemingly, or even really, incompatible elements occur more often than not. The enemies of our enemies are our friends. Thus the Very Christian King of France allied himself with the Khalifa of Islam, Commander of the Faithful. Or to come back to the history of philosophico-scientific thought, what is more strange than the alliance of Mach and Eistein?

Democritean atoms in the space of Plato, or of Euclid: one understands that Newton needed a God in order to maintain the connection between the elements of his universe; one understands also, the rather curious character of this universe (the 19th century was too accustomed to it to be able to notice its strangeness) whose material elements, objects of a theoretical extrapolation of the experience, swim or are immersed,*without being affected by it,* in the nothingness of absolute space—a real and even necessary and eternal *non ens*—object of *a priori* intellectual knowledge. One understands therefore the rigorous mutual implication of this absolute, or of these absolutes—absolute space, absolute time, and absolute motion—that are accessible only to pure intellectual cognition, and their complementary opposites, relative space, relative time, relative motion that are the only ones given to us by empirical knowledge.

Modern science stands and falls with these conceptions of absolute time, absolute space, and their concomitants, absolute motion and absolute rest. Newton, as good a metaphysician as mathematician or physicist, recognized this perfectly well. And we can trust him in this case: only with these presuppositions and only on the basis of these fundamental assumptions are the *axioms* or *laws* of motion and of action valid and meaningful. The great Newtonians, Maclaurin and Euler, as well as the greatest of them, Laplace, fully recognized it too.

But let us come back to Newton. It is possible, according to him, that there is, perhaps, not one body in this our world that is really and truly at rest; moreover, even if there were one, we should not be able to recognize the fact and to distinguish it from a body in uniform motion. It is also true that we have no means, and can never have any, of determining the absolute motion of a body—its motion with respect to absolute space—but only and solely its relative motion, that is, its motion with respect to other bodies, about whose absolute motion we know no more than about that of the first. Yet these statements are not objections against these concepts; on the contrary, they are necessary and inevitable consequences of the very structure of their objects, that is, space and time. Moreover, Newton should not have been so prudent—although in the Newtonian world it is infinitely improbable that there ever should be a body at absolute rest and completely impossible that there should ever be one in uniform motion, Newtonian physics cannot avoid using these notions.

In the Newtonian world, and in Newtonian science—in spite of Kant who largely misinterpreted it but opened a way to a new epistemology and a new metaphysics, supporting a new science—the conditions of knowledge *do not* determine the conditions of being; quite the contrary, it is the srtucture of reality that determines which of our faculties of knowledge can possibly (or cannot) make it accessible to us.

Or, to use an old, Platonic formula: in the Newtonian world, and in Newtonian science, it is not man, but God who is the measure of things.

The interpretation of the history and structure of modern science that I have sketched here is not the *communis opinio doctorum*. At least not yet, though to judge by some recent publications, it is on the way to becoming just that.

Still, the prevailing trend of interpretation is somewhat different, and modern science is, as often as not, and even more often than not, presented as an example—*the* example —of empiricist or positivist epistemology. Historians and philosophers of the positivist school are wont to stress in the work of Galileo and of Newton (they usually pass over Descartes) their experimental aspect, presenting them as rejecting the search for *causes* and restricting the aim of science to the establishment of *laws;* not asking *why* something happens but *how* it happens.

This interpretation is certainly not lacking in historical basis; the role played by experience, or, more exactly, by experiment, in the history of science is more than obvious. Moreover, the works of Gilbert, Galileo, Robert Boyle, and others, are full of passages extolling the value and the fecundity of experimental methods and opposing them to the sterility of the speculative approach. And as for the restriction to the investigation of *laws* in preference to that of *causes,* everybody knows the famous passage from *Discourses and Mathematical Demonstrations concerning Two New Sciences* in which Galileo announces that it would be "unprofitable" for his purpose (which is, precisely, the establishment of the law of falling bodies) to discuss the explanations of gravity proposed and developed by his predecessors, just because nobody knows what gravity is—merely a word—and that, instead of trying to find out *why bodies fall,* it is much better to content ourselves with determining the mathematical law of their downward motion.

And everybody knows, too, the even more famous passages of the *Philosophiae Naturalis Principia Mathematica* (scholium) in which Newton says of gravity (which, meanwhile, has become universal gravitation) that hitherto he has not "been able to discover the cause of these properties of gravity from phenomena." He writes:

I feign no hypotheses, for whatever is not deduced from the phenomena is to be called a hypothesis, and hypotheses, whether metaphysical or physical, whether of occult qualities or mechanical have no place in experimental philosophy. In this philosophy particular propositions are inferred from the phenomena and afterwards rendered general by induction.

In other terms, relations established by experiments, or observation, are, by induction, transformed into laws.

Thus it is by no means surprising that, for a great number of historians and philosophers, this legalistic and phenomenalistic aspect of modern science appeared to constitute its essence, or at least its *proprium,* in contradistinction to the deductive and realistic science of the Middle Ages and of antiquity. Closely linked with it appeared also the pragmatic, active, technologic aspect of modern science—*scientia activa, operativa* of Bacon—as opposed to the allegedly contemplative, "theoretical" science of the past.

To this interpretation I have already made some objections. Two other objections are also pertinent.

1) Whereas the legalistic trend of modern science is indubitable, and besides has been extremely fruitful since it enabled the scientists of the eighteenth century to concentrate upon the study and analysis of the fundamental laws of the

Newtonian universe, a work that culminated in the *Mécanique céleste* of Laplace and the *Mécanique analytique* of Lagrange, its phenomenalistic aspect is much less apparent: as a matter of fact it is not the *phenomena*, but the *noumena* or the *noeta* that find themselves bound together by the causally unexplained or even unexplainable laws. Indeed, not bodies of our common-sense world, but abstract, Archimedean bodies of the Galilean one, or the particles and atoms of the Newtonian world, are the *relata* or the *fundamenda* of the mathematical relations established by modern science. Moreover, and this changes the picture somewhat, the *law* of attraction was transformed by the successors of Newton into a *cause* or *force*.

2) The positivist interpretation or self-interpretation of science is by no means "modern." Quite the contrary: it is nearly as old as science itself, and like everything, or nearly everything, was invented by the Greeks, (as Schiaparelli and especially Duhem, after others, have quite convincingly established); the purpose of astronomical science, Alexandrine astronomers explained, is *not* to find out the real mechanism of planetary motion but only to σώξειν τά φαινόμενα, to save the phenomena by putting together a system of circles—a purely mathematical device—enabling us to calculate and predict the position of the planets, and thus establish a connection between the data of previous and future observations.

It is just this positivist-pragmatist epistemology that was used by Osiander (in 1543) in order to hide behind it the revolutionary impact of Copernican astronomy, and it was against this phenomenalistic misinterpretation that was directed the emphasis of the founders of modern science from Kepler who puts ΑΙΤΙΟΛΟΓΕΤΟΣ in the very title of his work and calls it *Physica Coelestis*, to Newton who, in spite of his *hypotheses non fingo* that I have just quoted, gives us in the *Mathematical Principles of Natural Philosophy* not only a realistic, but also a causal science. He does this simply because, though he had renounced finding out the mechanical explanation of attraction and even rejected its reality as a physical force acting at a distance, he nevertheless posits it as a real, though nonmechanical and probably transphysical one, that subtends the mathematical "force" which binds the world together.

The real ancestor of positivist physics is by no means Newton. It is Malebranche.

Indeed, the Newtonian attitude concerning the problem of attraction is incompatable with the positivist point of view. For, from this point of view, there is no problem at all. Action at a distance, and even instantaneous action at a distance, which Newton so strongly opposed, is just as unobjectionable as any other kind of causation. E. Mach long ago, and P. W. Bridgman more recently and much more radically, have made it perfectly clear: to ask for continuity in space or in time is to be bound by prejudice.

As a matter of fact, this attitude has never been that of science. Action at a distance, even for those of the Newtonians who, following Cotes, accepted it as a physical force, has always been felt as something strange and difficult to admit—an absurdity to which one gets accustomed remains nevertheless an absurdity—and it is this conviction, which, by the way, could make an appeal to the authority of Newton himself, that consciously inspired the work of Euler, of Faraday and Maxwell, and finally that of Einstein, who, by joining together the disconnected elements of the Newtonian world, space and matter, eventually solved the riddle.

So it seems to me that, in this case as in a number of others, it was not the positivist renunciation, nor the pressure of technical development of mathematical and experimental methods and procedures, but a philosophical attitude, that of *mathematical realism,* that has been the driving force or source of inspiration of the post-Newtonian development of scientific thought, the root of the concept of "field," that new key-concept of which Einstein has shown us the capital value for present-day science.

Thus I believe that we are entitled to conclude, tentatively at least, that: (i) the positivistic phase of renouncement, or resignation, is only a kind of retreat position, and it is always a temporary one; (ii) although the human mind, in its pursuit of knowledge, repeatedly assumes this attitude, it does not accept it as final—at least it has never done so until now; and (iii) sooner or later it ceases to make virtue of necessity and congratulate itself on its defeat. Sooner or later it comes back to the allegedly unprofitable, impossible, or meaningless task and tries to find a causal and real explanation of the accepted and established laws. And this, after all, is not surprising, at least for those who recognize that man is not only ποιημιχόν, a being of action, but also and perhaps even primarily, ζῷον λογιχόν, a being of reason, and that by nature there is in man the desire not only to know but to understand.

The Dual Role of the Zeitgeist

in Scientific Creativity

by Edwin G. Boring

THIS "magic" term *Zeitgeist* means at any one time the climate of opinion as it affects thinking, yet it is also more than that, for the *Zeitgeist* is forever being altered, as if the thinker whom it affects were shifting latitude and longitude over sea and land so that his climate keeps changing in unpredictable ways. Goethe, who in 1827 may have been the first to use this word with explicit connotation, limited it to the unconscious, covert, and implicit effects of the climate of opinion, at the same time ruling out thought control by such explicit processes as persuasion and education (*1*).

Such a concept proves useful in those cases where plagiarism is clearly unconscious, as so often it is. No man clearly understands the sources of his own creativity, and it is only since Freud that we have begun to have an inkling of how general is this lack of understanding of one's own motives and of the sources of one's own ideas. On the other hand, this conception long antedates Freud, for it was the essence of Tolstoy's argument in 1869 that "a king is history's slave" whose conscious reasons for action are trivial and unimportant. Charles Darwin, Herbert Spencer, and Francis Galton all supported Tolstoy's view of the unconscious determination of the actions of great men, against the more voluntaristic views of Thomas Carlyle, William James, and some lesser writers.

Later the historians of science and of thought in general found themselves faced with the essential continuity of originality and discovery. Not only is a new discovery seldom made until the times are ready for it, but again and again it turns out to have been anticipated, inadequately perhaps but nevertheless explicitly, as the times were beginning to get ready for it. Thus the concept of a gradually changing *Zeitgeist* has been used to explain the historical continuity of thought and the observation that the novelty of a discovery, after the history of its anticipations has been worked out, appears often to be only a historian's artifact.

In addition to these anticipations there are, however, also the near-simultaneities and near-synchronisms that are clearly not plagiarisms. Napier and Briggs on logarithms. Leibnitz and Newton on the calculus. Boyle and Mariotte on the gas law. D'Alibard and Franklin on electricity. The sociologists Ogburn and Thomas have published a list of 148 contemporaneous but independent discoveries or inventions. Since you cannot in these pairs assume that one man got the crucial idea from the other, you are forced to assume that each had his novel insight independently by his ordinary processes of thought, except that each was doing his thinking in the same climate of opinion. Some such appeal to a maturing *Zeitgeist* is necessary to explain the coincidence (2).

Now how, we may ask, does the *Zeitgeist* of the present time interpret the generic concept of the *Zeitgeist*? Today the *Zeitgeist* is certainly *not* a superorganic soul, an immortal consciousness undergoing maturation with the centuries, an unextended substance interpenetrating the social structure. The *Zeitgeist* must be regarded simply as the sum total of social interaction as it is common to a particular period and a particular locale. One can say it is thought being affected by culture, and one would mean then that the thinking of every man is affected by the thinking of other men in so far as their thinking is communicated to him. Hence the importance of communication in science, which both helps and hinders progress. That is the thesis of this paper.

It is always hard to be original, to make progress in a minority thinking that goes against the majority. In science, moreover, even the dead help to make up the majority, for they communicate by the printed word and by the transmitted conventions of thought. Thus the majority, living and dead, may slow up originality. On the other hand, the chief effect of scientific communication and of the availability of past thought is facilitative. We all know how the invention of printing advanced science.

We shall not be far wrong—being prejudiced, of course,

by the *Zeitgeist* of the present—if we regard the scientist as a nervous system, influenced by what it reads and hears as well as by what it observes in nature and in the conduct of other men—the smile of approbation, the sneer of contempt —and affected also by its own past experience, for the scientist is forever instructing himself as he proceeds toward discovery and is also forever being instructed by other men, both living and dead.

The single investigator works pretty much like a rat in a maze—by insight, hypothesis, trial, and then error or success. I am not trying to say that rats are known to prefer deduction to induction because they use hypotheses in learning a maze. The maze is set up to require learning by trial and error, which is to say, by hypothesis and test. The rat's insight, as it learns, may indeed be false: the rat looks down the alley, sees it is not immediately blind but later finds it is blind after all. An error for the rat. And its trial may be vicarious. The rat looks tentatively down an alley, entertains it as a hypothesis, rejects it, chooses to go the other way. Anybody's hypothesis can come as the brilliant perception of an unexpected relationship and yet be wrong. It may be a hunch. Rodent hypotheses begin as hunches—and by this I mean merely that the rate does not understand the ground of its motives.

The human investigator, on the other hand, may consciously base his new hypothesis on his own earlier experiment, or on something other persons did. For this reason erudition is important, and communication is vital in modern science. Nevertheless it remains possible to regard the single scientist as an organic system, as a discovery machine, with a certain input from the literature and from other forms of social communication and also—let the essential empiricism of science not be forgotten—from nature, which comes through to insights and a conclusion by that method of concomitant variation which is experiment. There we have the individual investigator, who, as he grows older, gains in erudition and wisdom and becomes more mature, with his past discoveries now available as part of his knowledge.

A broader and more interesting question, however, concerns, not the individual, but the maturation of scientific thought itself. The mechanics of one person applies to too small a system to throw much light on the history of science.

The larger view substitutes social interaction and communication for an individual's input, thus exposing the whole dynamic process as it undergoes maturation down the years, the centuries, and the ages. This interaction *is* the *Zeitgeist*, which is not unlike a stream. It is bounded on its sides by the limits of communication, but it goes on forever unless, of course, some great cataclysm, one that would make Hitler's effect on German science seem tiny and trivial, should some day stall it.

Here we have a physicalistic conception of the *Zeitgeist*. The *Zeitgeist*, of course, inevitably influences the conception of the *Zeitgeist*. And the *Zeitgeist* ought to be the property of psychologists, for the psychologists have a proprietary right in all the *Geister*. Now the psychology of the nineteenth century was dualistic, mentalistic, spiritualistic. In those days the *Zeitgeist* would certainly have had to be the maturing superconsciousness of science, something comparable to the immediate private experience that everyone then believed he had. The twentieth century, on the other hand, at least since 1925, is physicalistic and behavioristic. Nowadays the term *behavioral sciences* is on everyone's lips and there is no English equivalent for *Geisteswissenschaften*.

Between 1910 and 1930 the *Zeitgeist* changed. Mind gave way to behavior. This transition was eased by the positivists who supplied the transformation equations from the old to the new, transformations by way of the operational definitions of experience; but only a few bother to use these equations. It is enough for most persons that they are using the convenient language of the great majority. And truth in science, as S. S. Stevens has pointed out, is simply what competent opinion at the time in question does not dissent from (*3*). In a physicalistic era, we, physicalistically minded scientists, choose a physicalistic definition of the *Zeitgeist*. Our predecessors in 1900 would not so easily have accepted such nonchalance toward Cartesian dualism.

We are wise thus to accept the wisdom of the age. Nor is my personal history without interest in this respect, for I was brought up in the introspective school of E. B. Titchener and for twenty years believed firmly in the existence of my own private immediate consciousness. Then, about 1930, en route to Damascus, as it were, I had a great insight. I knew that I was unconscious and never had been conscious in the sense that to have experience is to know instantaneously that you have it. Introspection always takes time, and the most immediate conscious datum is, therefore, obtained retrospectively. Once this basic truth is assimilated, once one realizes that no system can include the report of itself and that to one's own introspection one's own consciousness is as much the consciousness of some "Other One" as is the consciousness of a different person, then it becomes clear that consciousness is not in any sense immediate, and then —just exactly then—the introspectionist gladly and sincerely joins the behavioristic school (4).

The *Zeitgeist* has a dual role in scientific progress, sometimes helping and sometimes hindering. There can be nothing surprising in such a statement. Forces in themselves are not good or bad. Their effects can be, depending on what it is you want. Inevitably by definition the *Zeitgeist* favors conventionality, but conventionality itself keeps developing under the constant pressures of discoveries and novel insights. So the *Zeitgeist* works against originality; but is not originality, one asks quite properly, a good thing, something that promotes scientific progress? In the cases of Copernicus, Galileo, Newton, and other comparably great men of science, originality was good—good for what posterity has called progress. These are the men to emulate. The indubitably original people are, however, the cranks, and close to them are the paranoid enthusiasts. Velikovsky's conception of the collision of two worlds is original. Does science advance under his stimulus? Hubbard's dianetics is original. Is it good? Most of us right now think not, yet these men point in self-defense to Galileo who also resisted the *Zeitgeist* (5). This dilemma arises because it is well to know and respect the wisdom of the ages and also to correct it when the evidence for change is adequate. If men were logical machines and evidence could be weighed in balances, we should not be mentioning the *Zeitgeist* at all. The *Zeitgeist* comes into consideration because it can on occasion work irrationally to distort the weight of the evidence.

When does the *Zeitgeist* help and when does it hinder the progress of science?

1) It is plain that knowledge helps research and knowledge, whether it be explicit on the printed page of a handbook or implicit in the unrecognized premises of a theory, is in the *Zeitgeist*. There is no use trying to limit the *Zeitgeist*

to that knowledge which you have without knowing it, for the line simply cannot be kept. One discovery leads to another, or one experiment leads to a theory that leads to another experiment, and the history of science tells the story. The law of multiple proportions, for instance, validates the atomic theory, and then the atomic theory leads off to all sorts of chemical research and discovery.

On the other hand, the *Zeitgeist* does not always help, for there is bad knowledge as well as good, and it takes good knowledge to get science ahead. It is useful to be ignorant of bad knowledge.

The idea that white is a simple color was a bit of bad knowledge that was in the *Zeitgeist* in the middle of the seventeenth century. It was not a silly idea. It was empirically based. You can see colors, can you not? And white is a color. And you can see that it is simple and not a mixture, can you not? It is not clear whether Newton was lucky enough not to have absorbed this bit of false knowledge from the *Zeitgeist* or whether he was just stubborn, when, having bought his prism at the Stourbridge Fair, he concluded that white is a mixture of other colors. He was probably consciously flouting the *Zeitgeist,* for he sent his paper up to the Royal Society with the remark that it was in his "judgment the oddest if not the most considerable detection which hath hitherto been made into the operations of nature." But Robert Hooke and the others at the Royal Society would have none of it. They were restrained from belief by the *Zeitgeist.* White is obviously not colored, not a mixture. There was bitter controversy before the conventional scientists gave in, before the truth shifted over to Newton's side (6).

Helmholtz ran into a similar difficulty when in 1850 he measured the velocity of the nervous impulse. The *Zeitgeist* said: The soul is unitary; an act of will is not spread out over a period of time; you move your finger; you do not will first that the finger move with the finger not moving until the message gets to it. Thus, Helmholtz' father had religious scruples against accepting his son's discovery. And Johannes Müller, then the dean of experimental physiology, doubted that the conduction times could be so slow. At the very least, he thought, the rate of the impulse must approximate the speed of light (7).

The persistence of the belief in phlogiston is still another example of the inertia that the *Zeitgeist* imposes on progress in thought. Here both Lavoisier and Priestley broke away from convention enough to discover oxygen, but Lavoisier, with the more negativistic temperament, made the greater break and came farther along toward the truth, whereas Priestley could not quite transcend his old habits of thought. His theory was a compromise, whereas we know now—insofar as we ever know truth in science—that that compromise was not the way to push science ahead then (8).

So it is. Good knowledge promotes progress, bad knowledge hinders, and both kinds make up the *Zeitgeist*. Ignorance of good knowledge and awareness of bad hinder; awareness of good and ignorance of bad help. The history of science is full of instances of all four.

2) Not only do the discovery of fact and the invention of theory help progress when fact and theory are valid, but comparable principles apply to the discovery and invention of new scientific techniques. The telescope seems to have come out of the *Zeitgeist,* for it was invented independently by half a dozen different persons in 1608, although lenses had been made and used for magnification for at least 300 years. But then Galileo's discovery of Jupiter's moons the next year created, as it were, a new phase in the *Zeitgeist,* one that promoted astronomical discovery. So it was with the invention of the simple microscope, the compound microscope, the Voltaic pile, the galvanic battery, the galvanometer, the electromagnet, and recently the electron tube —the possibilities opened up by the availability of a new important instrument change the atmosphere within a field of science and lead quickly to a mass of valid research. Within psychology the experimental training of a rat in a maze in 1903, in order to measure its learning capacity, led at once to a long series of studies in the evolution of animal intelligence with the maze as the observational instrument.

It is true that the negative instances of this aspect of the *Zeitgeist* are not so frequent or obvious; yet they occur. For years the Galton whistle, used for the determination of the upper limit of hearing, was miscalibrated, because its second harmonic had been mistaken for its first. The highest audible pitch was thought to occur at about 40,000 cycles per second, whereas the correct figure is about 20,000. Did this error of an octave hold back science? Not much, but a little. For a couple of decades investigators reported facts about the octave above 20,000 cycles per second, an octave that is really inaudible. One experimenter even found a special vowel quality for it to resemble. Thus bad knowledge about the whistle led to confusion and hindered the advance of science.

3) The *Zeitgeist* acts as inertia in human thinking. It makes thought slow but also surer. As a rule scientific thinking does not suddenly depart widely from contemporary opinion. In civilization, as in the individual, the progress of thought is sensibly continuous. Consider, for example, the history of the theory of sensory quality.

Empedocles believed that eidola of objects are transmitted by the nerves to the mind so that it may perceive the objects by their images. Later there arose the notion that there are animal spirits in the nerves to conduct the eidola. Then, under the influence of materialism, the animal spirits came to be regarded as a *vis viva* and presently a *vis nervosa*. Next Johannes Müller, seeing that every sensory nerve always produces its own quality, substituted for the *vis nervosa* five specific nerve energies, using the word *energy*, in the days before the theory of conservation of energy, as equivalent to *force* or *vis*. He said that the mind, being locked away in the skull, cannot perceive the objects themselves, or their images, but only the states of the nerves that the objects affect, and he fought a battle against the Empedoclean theory—as indeed had John Locke and Thomas Young and Charles Bell before him, and as still others were to do after him. After a while it was seen, however, that the specificity of the five kinds of nerves lies not in the peculiar energies that they conduct to the brain but in where they terminate in the brain. Thus there arose the concept of sensory centers in the cerebrum. Nowadays we see that a cerebral center is nothing more than a place where connections are made and that sensory quality must be understood in terms of the discriminatory response in which stimulation eventuates—or at least many of us see this fact while we fight a *Zeitgeist* that still supports the theory of centers (9).

Is there any reason why Galen in A.D. 180 or Albrecht von Haller in 1766 should not have invented the modern theory of sensory quality? None, except that most of the supporting evidence was lacking and, being contrary to the accepted notions of the time, it would have sounded silly. Yet each contributor to this strand of scientific maturation as original, and several contributors had to fight again ne battle against the notion that the mind perceives an object by embracing it, or, if it cannot get at the object itself, by etting itself impressed by the object's eidolon or simulacum. Nor has the *Zeitgeist* even yet been thoroughly disciplined in this affair, as you can tell whenever you hear the emark: "If the lens of the eye inverts the image of the external world on the retina, why do we not see upside down?"

The *Zeitgeist* was hindering progress in this piece of history. It made originality difficult and it made it necessary to epeat the same arguments in 1690 (John Locke) and in 826 (Johannes Müller) and, if one may believe current dvertisements of a scientific film, nowadays too. Yet let us emember that this *Zeitgeist* also helped progress. The connuity of development lay always within the *Zeitgeist*. It as a conservative force that demanded that originality reain responsible, that it be grounded on evidence and available knowledge. Had Galen espoused a connectionist's view f sensory quality in the second century, he would have been responsibly original, a second-century crank, disloyal to ne truth as it existed then. Loyalty may be prejudice and ometimes it may be wrong, but it is nevertheless the stuff f which responsible continuous effort is made. Science eeds responsibility as well as freedom, and the *Zeitgeist* apports the one virtue even though it may impede the other.

4) What may be said of the big *Zeitgeist* may also be aid of the little *Zeitgeister* of schools and of the leaders of chools and of the egoist who has no following. They have neir inflexible attitudes and beliefs, their loyalties that are rejudices, and their prejudices that are loyalties. Every scintific in-group with strong faith in a theory or a method is microcosm, mirroring the macrocosm which is the larger orld of science.

Take egoism. Is it bad? It accounts for a large part of the rive that produces research, for the dogged persistence hat is so often the necessary condition of scientific success. o egoism yields truth. It accounts also for the hyperbole nd exaggeration of the investigating enthusiast, and then t may yield untruth. When two incompatible egoisms come ogether, they account for the wasted time of scientific warare, for the dethronement of reason by rationalization. Egoism is both good and bad.

Take loyalty. Think how it cements a group together and

promotes hard work. Yet such in-groups tend to shut them
selves off from other out-groups, to build up their specia
vocabularies, and so, while strengthening their own drive
to lessen communication with the outside, the communica
tion that advances science. Loyalty is both good and bad
and with loyalty a person sometimes has to choose whethe
he will eat his cake or will keep it.

This dilemma posed by the little *Zeitgeister* of the in
groups and the scientific evangelists has its root in basi
psychological law. Attention to this is inevitably inattentio
to that. Enthusiasm is the friend of action but the enemy o
wisdom. Science needs to be both concentrated and diffuse
both narrow and broad, both thorough and inclusive. Th
individual investigator solves this problem as best he ca
each according to his own values, as to when to sell breadt
in order to purchase depth and when to reverse the transac
tion. He, the individual, has limited funds and he has t
sell in order to buy, and he may never know whether h
made the best investment. But posterity will know, at lea
better than he, provided that it troubles to assess the matte
at all, for posterity, having only to understand without har
labor, can assess the effect of prejudice and loyalty and er
thusiasm, of tolerance and intolerance, as no man ever ca
in himself.

Coda

This is a broad meaning for the word *Zeitgeist*—the tota
body of knowledge and opinion available at any time to
person living within a given culture. There is, certainly, n
rigorous way of distinguishing between what is explicit
a scientist and what is implicit in the forms and patterns o
communication, between what is clear conclusion and wha
is uncritically accepted premise. Available knowledge
communicated whenever it becomes effective, and this
the *Zeitgeist* working.

The *Zeitgeist* is a term from the language of dualism
while its definition is formally physicalistic. That parado
is for the sake of convenience in the present communicatio
and is allowable because every statement can be tran
formed into physicalistic language when necessary. Dualis
has the disadvantage of implying a mystery, the existence o
a *Zeitgeist* as a vague supersoul pervading and controllin
the immortal body of society. We need no such nonsens

ven though this abstinence from mystery reduce us to so
rdinary a concept as a *Zeitgeist* inclusive of all available
nowledge that affects a thinker's thinking.

That such a *Zeitgeist* sometimes helps progress and some-
imes hinders it should be clear by now. As a matter of fact,
he distinction between help and hindrance can never be
bsolute but remains relative to some specific goal. The
Zeitgeist hindered Copernicus, who, resisting it, helped scintific thought onward and presently changed the *Zeitgeist*
n this matter to what it was in Newton's day. Did the *Zeitgeist* that Newton knew help relativity theory? No; relativity
ad to make its way against that *Zeitgeist*. The newest
Zeitgeist, which will include the principles of relativity and
ncertainty and complementarity, presumably exists today
vithin the in-group of theoretical physicists. It will become
eneral eventually, and then it will reinforce progress, and
fter that, much later, perhaps our posterity will find today's
ruth tomorrow's error. The one sure thing is that science
eeds all the communication it can get. The harm commu-
ication does to progress never nearly equals the good.

NOTES

. The term *Zeitgeist* seems to have originated in this sense in 1827
with Goethe who, in discussing the way in which Homer had influenced thought, remarked in the last sentence of his essay,
Homer noch einmal, "Und dies geschieht denn auch im Zeit-
geiste, nicht verabredet noch überliefert, sondern *proprio motu,*
der sich mehrfälig unter verschiedenen Himmelsstrichen hervor-
tut." *Himmelsstrichen* can be translated "climates," thus justify-
ing the figure of the text, but it must also be noted that Goethe
meant to use the term *Zeitgeist* when the effect is "self-deter-
mined," brought about "neither by agreement nor fiat." See, for
instance, *Goethes sämtliche Werke* (I. J. Cotta, Berlin, 1902–
07), vol. 38, p. 78.
. The discussion of this paragraph and all the references will be
found *in extenso* in E. G. Boring, "Great men and scientific
progress," *Proc. Am. Phil. Soc.* **94,** 339 (1950). The reference to
Tolstoy is, of course, to his *War and Peace.* For the longest list
of nearly simultaneous inventions and discoveries, see W. F.
Ogburn and D. Thomas, "Are inventions inevitable?" *Polit. Sci.
Quart.* **37,** 83 (1922).
. On the social criterion of truth, on scientific truth's being what
scientists agree about, see S. S. Stevens, "The operational basis of
psychology," *Am. J. Psychol.* **47,** 323 (1935), especially p. 327;
"The operational definition of psychological concepts," *Psychol.*

Rev. **42**, 517 (1935), especially p. 517; E. G. Boring, "The validation of scientific belief," *Proc. Am. Phil. Soc.* **96**, 535 (1952), especially pp. 537 f.

4. On the point that a self cannot observe itself, that in self-observation a person must regard himself as if he were another person, see M. Meyer, *Psychology of the Other One* (Missouri Book Co., Columbia, Mo., 1921); Stevens, *op. cit.*, especially pp. 328 f.; E. G. Boring, "A history of introspection," *Psychol. Bull.* **50**, 169 (1953), especially p. 183.

5. On the sincerity of cranks in science, see I. B. Cohen, J. L. Kennedy, C. Payne-Gaposchkin, T. M. Riddick, and E. G. Boring, "Some unorthodoxies of modern science," *Proc. Am. Phil. Soc.* **96**, 505 (1952).

6. On Newton's difficulty in changing the *Zeitgeist* with respect to the complexity of white, see E. G. Boring, *Sensation and Perception in the History of Experimental Psychology* (Appleton-Century, New York, 1942), pp. 101 f. This discovery of Newton's was exceptional in that it had no anticipations (unless my wisdom is at fault). In other words, the *Zeitgeist* was strongly fixed, and to break it Newton must have been very stubborn—as indeed other evidence indicates that he was.

7. On Helmholtz' trouble with the *Zeitgeist* with respect to the velocity of the nervous impulse, see E. G. Boring, *A History of Experimental Psychology* 2 ed. (Appleton-Century-Crofts, New York, 1950), pp. 41 f., 47 f.

8. On Priestley and Lavosier and the *Zeitgeist's* support of the phlogiston theory, see J. B. Conant, *The Overthrow of the Phlogiston Theory,* Harvard Case Histories in Experimental Science, Case 2 (Harvard Univ. Press, Cambridge, Mass., 1950).

9. On the history of the physiological theories of sensory quality and the retardation of progress in thinking by successive phases of this *Zeitgeist*, see E. G. Boring, *Sensation and Perception (op. cit.),* pp. 68–83, 93–95.

Alternative Interpretations of the

History of Science

by Robert S. Cohen

In proposing several general questions on the social and historical aspects of science, I hope to state certain problems that have only too obvious a bearing on our work in the inerpretation of science, to indicate certain alternative solutions to these problems that have been proposed before, and to urge that certain of these are at best incomplete while the others are still merely plausible (*1*).

The achievement of understanding of the social relations of science is a scientific problem that lies in the sciences of history and sociology. But it is not a problem solely in the history of science nor in the sociology of science even when the former is widened to include external (nonscientific) influences on the development of science. As in the solution of all scientific problems, this one involves data and theories. Thus the historisociological events need to be established and while some primitive theory may be involved in the selection of epochs or regions to be investigated, yet there is a major fact-finding job for the student of the history of science. Utilizing these results, as well as those from other investigations, even from other sciences, the historian may be expected to formulate theories that explain how and why science developed including its mutually effective relations with the social (and sometimes physical and biological) environment. And we may expect some deliberate choice of specific historical investigations to lend credence to or to offer discrediting evidence about these explanatory interpretations.

I am neither a historian nor a sociologist, and at a symposium of the unity of science movement, I can only join with those who are deploring the extraordinary lack of detailed studies in the history of the social relations of science. I can only regret that the sociology of knowledge, and especially of science, has remained so long outside that movement's sweep, and so largely in the hands of metaphysically oriented phenomenologists and other speculative thinkers. The early death of Edgar Zilsel, a pioneer in the sociological treatment of science, left his work (*2*) tragically incomplete.

H. Guerlac has described an essential testing ground of certain theories about the development of science, namely the effect of political structure, and, *a fortiori,* of revolutionary changes in political structure, on science. E. G. Boring has considered the positive and negative influences of cultural milieu or *Zeitgeist* on the individual creation of scientific ideas and perhaps on activities of individuals and groups. And A. Koyré has focused this diffuse cultural in-

200 / The Validation of Scientific Theories

fluence upon that aspect which has been so very importan in western Europe science, namely philosophic systems o philosophic outlooks.

I want to suggest what probably none of these writer would deny, that each article is part of a broader approach which relates the total aspects of society to science; and shall offer a scheme which, because it is very simple, ca relate the three articles and suggest certain problems an points of departure (3). Then I shall briefly apply thi scheme to two particular scientific concepts.

The impacts of the sciences *on the social order* have per haps been most often examined, and are known to take many forms, direct and indirect. I will, in view of this, turn my attention to the impact of the social order *on science*. In studying the role of the social environment, past and present vis-a-vis science, it is just as well to state boldly what we want to know about the state of science in some detail namely, why the following aspects exist as they do: (i) the social position of the scientific enterprise; (ii) the internal social characteristics of science, the variety and quantity o talent, the institutional forms, including professional socie ties and mediums of communications, forms of training and education of scientists, and of the public, and so forth; (iii' why certain problems are dealt with; (iv) why certain solu tions (concepts and theories) are offered at the time they are offered; (v) why certain solutions are accepted; and (vi) why a mode of explanation is accepted, dominating the judgment of a man, a school or an epoch.

It is, of course, important to distinguish the sources o problems from the sources of answers and solutions to these problems. Likewise it is necessary to realize that we seek the historical genesis of these problems and of their solu tions. Explanation of the history of scientific thought and practice will be genetic explanation (at least until historica explanation generally advances to now unknown charac teristics).

The source of problems and solutions are of only two kinds, which may operate jointly in complex fashion and may be difficult to disentangle: (i) those due to previous stages of science, including of course other scientific activi ties, not logically connected to the particular scientific activ ity we seek to explain, and (ii) those due to nonscientific factors.

There is another way of typifying the sources: (i) those internal to the science, and that generate a problem logically, and (ii) those that pose problems only by external circumstance, in which case the neighboring sciences form part of the external group. Those who have explored the external factors have suggested a wide variety of social influences on science: the influence of religion—Max Weber, R. K. Merton, C. Raven, G. N. Clark, S. F. Mason, and W. Pagel (4); the influence of art—L. L. Whyte, Herbert Read, and occasionally A. N. Whitehead (5); the effect of social institutions—Thorstein Veblen, Max Weber, and Lewis Mumford (6); the influence of philosophy—Plato, J. S. Haldane, J. Maritain, A. Koyré, E. Meyerson, J. Nef, and F. S. C. Northrop (7); the influence of the economic order and its cultural and ideologic reflections—Karl Marx (8); the distortion of political institutions and misconceptions of other sciences—K. Popper, M. Polanyi, F. Hayek (9); the influence of social images projected into nature—H. Kelsen (10); the influence of irrational choices of occupation and content—S. Freud, H. Sachs, C. G. Jung, and G. Bachelard (11).

All of these have been documented sufficiently and we may now ask that some comparative analysis be made. The significant hypothesis today, and for some time past, would be one which tries to determine the relations of dominance —for a specific period of science, or even a specific scientific event—among the many factors that have been suggested. The sweeping views of a Whitehead that the bifurcation of mind-body can be traced to Cartesian philosophy; or of Northrop that the science and general culture can be determined by an epistemological decision about the apprehension of nature; or of Freud's irrational determinants, or of the others, need to be put to a test which is somewhat different from that which they themselves offer. By this I mean that their exposition seems to be incomplete.

We must ask Koyré and Whitehead why a new philosophy of the cosmos, a science that uses material, unspiritual, and non-mental substance, gains dominance? Why and where does it arise? We must ask Northrop, why should an epistemological policy be *proposed* in the first place—surely not because of a previous epistemological decision—and why should it have been *accepted* as orthodox or normal in the second place? Or, would Northrop claim that the history of epistemology has an independent development from which the history of culture, and indeed general history, is derivative?

To put these questions more generally, we must ask why the undoubted relations I have just listed between science and the many aspects of social and individual life, exist as they do. Thus the study of the history of science must be carried on as part of the study of the history of general culture. For example, the study of the influence of religion on science—productive or restrictive—is only a step toward the study of the history of religion, not in a mere descriptive sense as a sequence of stages that no doubt influence science, but as part of cultural history in its own right, with its own demand for knowing why the religious forms developed as they have. Only if the history of religion is shown to be independent, or else dependent on still another aspect of society, will the religious explanation of scientific endeavors approach completeness. (Of course, if the history of religion is not independent and self-generating, then we must ask the same question of the historian of the sources of religion, in his turn.)

In the history of science there have been problems which, looked at logically and with hindsight, demanded treatment and yet were not considered by scientists; or, if they were considered, no headway was made either in theoretical treatment or in accumulation of evidence; or, again, that theory which satisfied an earlier scientific public seemed to a later scientist only to add to the puzzle (12). As often as not the later examination with changed criterions provided the stimulus to more comprehensive theory and more thorough research. Contrary to the thesis of Boring, I would say that men always go with the *Zeitgeist;* when they seem to oppose it, they do so within it, not against it, thereby revealing contradictory tendencies within it. We, as self-conscious and society-conscious thinkers, recognize that the sources of creative scientific theory—the ideas, analyses, visions of models, formal systems, experimental devices, and so forth— may exist in any aspect of human experience whatsoever (13); and we are receptive to the notion that all human events, even creative acts, have their genesis in other ascertainable parts of human culture.

How can we protect scientific knowledge from its varied

historical origins and influences? We may be tempted to use a principle of verification, and with it to recognize the cumulative nature and logical rigor of science. But I doubt that the verification principle taken by itself is sufficient to shield science. If we disregard the question, "*Should* empirical practice serving as verification be the filter for distinguishing true from false ideas?" we must recognize that: (i) only those truths (and falsehoods) can be filtered which a given environment provides (including internal as well as external factors), and error by omission and distortion may be great; (ii) the standards for judging truth are social products, and hence Boring's *Zeitgeist* is a product of the *Zeitgeist;* (iii) practice has not, in fact, been the test for all the accepted truths of Western science, not even some contemporary science.

We have, then, to distinguish three stages in the social influencing of scientific ideas: (i) the problem that is attacked; (ii) the ideas and techniques brought to bear on it; and (iii) the principles of verification that the society, as part of its culture, provides. To free our science from its own sociocentric predicament would require as much attention to the third, sociology of epistemology, as to the distortions introduced by the second, and the sins of omission in the first. And even then it is only a hypothesis that such self-knowledge would release a greater science than the past, in the sense that, perhaps prior knowledge, even self-knowledge, may at times be insufficient or unnecessary or even hostile to the production of knowledge.

My own feeling is that social conditions external to science act in two ways. In the first place, they are obviously sufficient to pose problems and direct the course of science or to frustrate it utterly. In the second place, what is less evident, they are necessary for solving problems, as sources both of ideas and of a verification principle. I shall sketch two examples briefly.

The development of the first two laws of thermodynamics came long after the scientific data were available, and they arose because of the social stimulation of steam power engineering on three men who were not fixed in their researches and thinking by the orthodox physics and chemistry of their day (*14*). Carnot was deliberately and explicitly seeking to improve the efficiency of the steam engine when he formulated the second law in 1824. Joule, in reaching the first law, correlated electric energy with mechanical work and then with heat in an attempt to make an electric engine that would be more efficient than a steam engine; and by 1843 the juggling of these ideas into a mechanical equivalent of heat had occurred. Mayer, as a ship's doctor, found in 1841 a need to suppose a mechanical equivalent of heat in discussing vital processes akin to combustion, and quite the same data as Lavoisier had used sixty years before. But, as Lilley puts the matter so well, Mayer viewed the body as a heat engine, Lavoisier viewed it as a furnace or fire. Mayer even used the steam locomotive analogy as a persuasive argument for the reader.

All these early discoverers of the conservation of energy, Carnot, Mayer, and Joule, argued that *vis viva,* (or twice our kinetic energy) was too important to be destroyed, quite like advocates in earlier centuries had argued about material substance. The same argument was not offered by Rumford in 1798, yet it seemed so natural in 1840 as itself to need no support. The cultural climate was so sharply different that Rumford, while discussing the generation of heat by mechanical friction, never seems to have thought about the converse effect, namely the generation of mechanical motion by heat, even though the steam engine was already in some use and even though he was active in applying science to practical affairs. It was the wide growth of engineering research by nonscientists and the change in the *Zeitgeist* which made possible the new explanation. Actually the explanation was couched in almost metaphysical language and in highly *a priori* terms; this is surely a sign that it was in the cultural air rather than actually *a priori*. It is notorious that the data did not prove the hypothesis of conservation of energy. The view that they did was based on arguments that would horrify an inductive statistician. The ways in which some scientific hypotheses and principles of high order and great importance have been brought to science and accepted by scientists should make a logical analyst shudder. The role of dogmatics, *a priori,* of analogies, and of new problems disconnected from previous science has often, in historical fact, been crucial.

The concept of laws of nature likewise exhibits social origins, both as problem and as hypothetical solution of the problem (15). The problem seems as old as magic and ever-present, namely why is the world so irregular, willful, and unpredictable? Or, are there regularities behind the veil of apparent irregularities and dissimilarities? If so, why the regularities? Now law, as a supreme legislation for the behavior of *natural* objects, arose in the ancient world along with a society that had just become centralized and capable of its own social legislation, namely the joint appearance of the Babylonian creation myth of Marduk and the Hammurabi legal code in 2000 B.C.

The pre-Socratics and Plato and Aristotle almost never used the idea of a law of nature (though they frequently used the notion of unlegislated and uncreated "natural" necessities or characteristics. By contrast they did have laws of men and gods). But the Stoics reintroduced law of nature again about 200 B.C., again at a time of political centralization in the new great Hellenistic monarchies. It was only plausible that Roman Stoics would continue this conception in the Roman empire, composed of many cultures and one law. Indeed the idea of an empirical natural law for all men and laws of nature for all nature was, broadly, a Roman commonplace. (Again the supreme law-giver of ancient Judaism and later Judeo-Christian ethical religion helped to give science its idea of law.) Note that the naturalistic Democriteans and Epicurus do not speak of laws of nature, for they have freed themselves from the social image of a creator. In all these, the laws of man and of nature are not separated. Indeed medieval writers often speak of animals as obeying a code laid down by God and of men as obligated to obey their human rulers only if the man-made laws conform with God's.

In modern science, the natural law as metaphor became explicitly so by the seventeenth century (and distinguished from human and moral laws of behavior of man), the first separation into metaphor occurring about the time of Kepler. Descartes speaks of the laws which God put into nature, Spinoza of the metaphor of Descartes, for Spinoza's pantheistic God could not easily be a lawgiver. Note that God, in earlier medieval time, was the divine will that brought the exceptions to the world, the *irregular* occurrences, for example comets and monsters. Now, after Descartes he is the lawgiver for the *regular* occurrences. Again the social model is the rise of a centralized political and legal authority, the new centralized nation-monarchies, the decline of local nobilities. As Zilsel pointed out, Descartes' idea of God as universal legislator occurred soon after Jean Bodin's new theory of sovereignty. The coincidence deserves careful examination from the historian of ideas.

The conception of an imposed law for nature originated in Oriental absolutism, declined in the Greek political fragmentation, flourished in the Greek and Roman world states, languished in medieval politically decentralized feudalism (despite religious centralization), and revived with the birth of capitalist international relations and centralized nation states, attaining a metaphysical status in its new naturalistic revival. Of course this quasitheological stage of science has now been abandoned, an event dramatized by Laplace's abandonment of the hypothesis of a universal legislator. We have now, in Pearson's phrase, descriptions instead of prescriptions. But could the recognition of statistical regularities and their mathematical expression have been reached by any other road than the theological one we actually traveled?

The only test comparison with a developed civilization is that of nontheological China. As Needham and Northrop have remarked, theology in China has been so depersonalized, law made so ethical, humanistic, and particular, that the idea of a rational creator of all things was not formulated. Hence the idea that we lesser rational beings might, by virtue of that Godlike rationality, be able to decipher the laws of nature (in Galileo's phrase, we might read the mathematical language of the Book of Nature) never was accepted.

The *Zeitgeist* of China exhibited a doctrine of harmony and of wholes, behavior in the natural expression of inner drives, not the impressed action of eternal and superior authority. China could have had a scientific theory of organism; if the other societal factors had given rise to a great activity aimed at understanding and controlling detailed natural processes (that is, science), it would have been functional at its base and probably non-mechanical. But if such scientific activity had been stimulated, theology might have developed too. And who can tell whether the theological mechanism was not really necessary to have naturalistic science, and mechanical science to have a science of process and organism? As Needham asked "Was the state of mind in which an egg-laying cock could be prosecuted at law necessary in a culture which later should have the property of producing a Kepler?"

NOTES

1. I am indebted to the Faculty Research Committee of Wesleyan University for grants which helped make possible the studies in the history and philosophy of science on which this article is based. A portion of this article was read as part of a paper presented to the Connecticut Section of the History of Science Society, 30 Oct. 1953.

2. The papers readily available in this country include: "History and biological evolution," *Phil. Sci.* **7**, 121 (1940); "Copernicus and mechanics," *J. Hist. Ideas* **1**, 113 (1940); "The origins of William Gilbert's scientific method," *ibid.* **2**, 1 (1941); "Phenomenology and natural science," *Phil. Sci.* **8**, 26 (1941); "Physics and the problem of historico-sociological laws," *ibid.* **8**, 567 (1941); "Development of empiricism," *International Encycl. Unified Science II* **8**, 53 (Univ. of Chicago Press, 1941); "The genesis of the concept of physical law" *Phil. Rev.* **51**, 245 (1942); "The sociological roots of science" *Am. J. Sociol.* **47**, 544 (1942); and "The genesis of the concept of scientific progress" *J. Hist. Ideas* **6**, 325 (1945). These and other writings of E. Zilsel will be edited under the general title *The Sociological Roots of Science* and introduced by a critical study of his work by R. S. Cohen (Routledge and Kegan Paul, London, 1957).

3. While writing these lecture notes for publication, two recent books came to my attention which are of direct relevance to the interpretation of science. Some of the issues I have raised are treated at greater length in them, and if this paper can call them to the attention of American scientists it will have been successful. One is the special issue, "Essays on the Social History of Science," of the Danish journal *Centaurus* **3**, 1–2 (1953–1954). Of relevance here are the essays by Childe ("Science in preliterate and the ancient Oriental civilizations"), Farrington ("The rise of abstract science among the Greeks"), Needham ("Thoughts on the social relations of science and technology in China"), Lilley ("Cause and effect in the history of science"), Taton ("The French revolution and the progress of science"), and Forbes ("Metallurgy and technology in the Middle Ages"). The second is J. D. Bernal, *Science and Industry in the Nineteenth Century* (Routledge and Kegan Paul, London, 1953), which contains a long title essay and a shorter acute discussion "Molecular asymmetry" given as homage to Pasteur. Bernal's book is noteworthy for its attempt at uncovering different types of technologic influence on the several sciences, and at different times in the course of the rise of the industrial

era, and at relating something of the reciprocal nature of these influences. In addition, several other works are promised that will shed light on these matters: *A History of Technology,* C. Singer, E. J. Holmyard, and A. R. Hall, Eds., to appear in 5 vols., of which vol. 1, *From Early Times to the Fall of Ancient Empires,* has been published (Oxford Univ. Press, 1954) and vol. 2, *The Mediterranean Civilization and the Middle Ages* will appear shortly; J. D. Bernal, *Science in History* (Watts, London, 1954); J. Needham, *Science and Civilization in China,* to appear in 7 vols., of which vol. 1, *Introductory Orientations,* and vol. 2, *History of Scientific Thought* (Cambridge Univ. Press, 1954 and 1956 respectively) have been published; and *Science, Medicine and History: Essays in Honor of Charles Singer,* 2 vol. (Oxford Univ. Press, 1954).

Needham's great work, just noted, is of interest as a comparative study of science in advanced cultures just as much as a lavish study of science in China; it will serve to adjudicate the claims of the various interpretations of the history of science mentioned in the present paper.

4. M. Weber, *The Protestant Ethic and the Spirit of Capitalism,* tr. Parsons (Allen and Unwin, London, 1948) especially note 145; R. K. Merton, "Puritanism, pietism and science" *Social. Rev.* **28**, 1 (1936) reprinted in his *Social Theory and Social Structure* (Free Press, Glencoe, Ill., 1949), and "Science, technology and society in 17th century England" *Osiris* **4** part 2 (Bruges, Belgium, 1938); J. Needham, "Science, religion and socialism" and "Pure science and the idea of the holy" in his selected essays *Time, the Refreshing River* (Allen and Unwin, London, 1943); C. Raven, *Science and Religion* (Cambridge Univ. Press, Cambridge, 1952); S. F. Mason. "Science and religion in seventeenth century England" *Past and Present* **1** No. 3, 28 (1953); W. Pagel, "Religious motives in the medical biology of the seventeenth century, *"Bull. Inst. Hist. Med. 3* 97 (1935) and *The Religious and Philosophical Aspects of van Helmont's Science and Medicine* (Suppl. No 2 to *Bull. Inst. Hist. Med.,* Johns Hopkins Press, Baltimore, 1944); *passim* in *Science, Religion and Reality,* J. Needham, ed. (new edition, Braziller, N. Y., 1955; orig. Sheldon Press, London, 1925).

5. L. L. Whyte, Ed., *Aspects of Form* (Lund Humphries and the Institute of Contemporary Arts, London, 1951); H. Read, *Art and Society,* rev. ed. (Faber and Faber, London, 1945); A. N. Whitehead, *Adventures of Ideas* (Macmillan, New York, 1943). M. Johnson, *Art and Scientific Thought* (Faber and Faber, London, 1946); W. M. Ivins, *Art and Geometry* (Cambridge: Harvard Univ. Press, 1946).

6. T. Veblen, *The Place of Science in Modern Civilization and Other Essays* (Viking Press, New York, 1919), and also J. Dorfman, *Thorstein Veblen and His America* (Viking Press, New

York, 1934); M. Weber, *op. cit.* (4), and also see his *From Max Weber: Essays in Sociology* (Oxford Univ. Press, New York, 1946); Lewis Mumford, *Technics and Civilization* (Harcourt, Brace, New York, 1934).

7. J. S. Haldane, *The Sciences and Philosophy* (Macmillan, London, 1926); J. Maritain, *Science and Wisdom* (Bles, London, 1944); E. Meyerson, *Identity and Reality* (Allen and Unwin, London, 1930); E. A. Burtt, *Metaphysical Foundations of Modern Physical Science,* rev. ed. (Routledge and Kegan Paul, London, 1932); F. S. C. Northrop, *The Meeting of East and West* (Macmillan, New York, 1946), and "The criterion of the good state," ch. 17 of *The Logic of the Sciences and the Humanities* (Macmillan, New York, 1947); the influence of general philosophical values turns out to be the theme of an essay little noticed by scientists, and which is initially devoted to the much discussed question of the coincidental rise of science and industrialism, J. U. Nef, "The genesis of industrialism and of modern science (1500–1640)" in *Essays in Honor of Conyers Read* (Univ. of Chicago Press, Chicago, 1953).

8. Karl Marx and Friedrich Engels, *The German Ideology* and also passages in Marx's *Capital,* vol. I (International Pub., New York, 1939); J. D. Bernal, *The Social Function of Science* (Routledge, London, 1939), and *Marx and Science* (Lawrence and Wishart, London, 1952); B. Hessen, "The social and economic roots of Newton's 'Principia'" in *Science at the Crossroads* (Kniga, London, 1931); A. R. Hall, *Ballistics in the Seventeenth Century* (Cambridge Univ. Press, Cambridge, 1952), a careful examination of the relations of science and war technology, which tends to confirm Bernal's cautious formulations of the Marxist thesis while casting doubt on the cruder work of Hessen, G. N. Clark, *Science and Social Welfare in the Age of Newton,* ed. 2 (Oxford Univ. Press, Oxford, 1949), a critical study of the Marxist thesis. It should, perhaps, be noted that the Marxist theory of scientific knowledge does not relegate all knowledge in capitalist or earlier societies to some ideological limbo of illusion, although the theory does imply that all knowledge is obtained from the perspective of the society which obtains it, and hence is distorted appropriately. It is an active research problem in Marxist sociology to determine the criterions for distortions and illusions as contrasted with the objective truths in a historically class-sponsored system of knowledge. The general view is that facts and mathematical formulas (to use the science of physics) are objective, but that the interpretation of the symbols tends to be ideologically distorted, for example the formulas of quantum mechanics as contrasted with the Bohr interpretation. For a popular provocative essay on this, see C. Caudwell, *The Crisis in Physics* (Bodley Head, London, 1939). I have discussed the Marx-

ist doctrine of ideological influence upon scientific thought, together with related issues, in "Dialectical materialism and Carnap's logical empiricism" to appear in *The Philosophy of Rudolf Carnap*, P. A. Schilpp, ed. (Tudor, New York, 1957).

9. K. R. Popper, *The Open Society and Its Enemies* (Routledge, London, 1945); M. Polanyi, *The Logic of Liberty* (Routledge and Kegan Paul, London, 1951); F. A. Hayek, *The Counter-Revolution of Science* (Free Press, Glencoe, Ill., 1952).

10. H. Kelsen, *Society and Nature* (Kegan Paul, London, 1946).

11. S. Freud, *Civilization and Its Discontents* (Hogarth Press, London, 1949), for example, p. 63, also his *The Future of an Illusion* (Hogarth Press, London, 1943) especially the concluding sections, and finally his *New Introductory Lectures on Psycho-Analysis* (Hogarth Press, London, 1949), especially Lecture 35. A few speculative essays in the psychoanalysis of science have been written, e.g. H. Sachs, "The delay of the machine age" *Psychoanal. Q.* **2**, 404–424 (1933) and "Über Naturgefühl" *Imago* **1** (1912), G. Bachelard, *La Formation de l'Esprit Scientifique* (Vrin, Paris, 1947) and *L'Eau et les Reeves* (J. Corti, Paris, 1942), and portions of H. Marcuse, *Eros and Civilization* (Beacon, Boston, 1955). See also the works of C. J. Jung, e.g. *Psychology and Alchemy,* tr. (Routledge and Kegan Paul, London, 1956).

12. See the chapter "The postponed scientific revolution in chemistry" in H. Butterfield, *The Origins of Modern Science 1300–1800* (Bell, London, 1949 and Macmillan, New York, 1950), and, for studies of scientific prophets before the times, see, in physics for example, D. W. Singer, *Giordano Bruno His Life and Thought* (Schuman, New York, 1950) and in history, H. P. Adams, *The Life and Writings of Giambattista Vico* (Allen and Unwin, London, 1938). The converse effect, namely very advanced technical accomplishments that could not be utilized until social demands reached a certain level of technologic competence, is discussed in A. R. Hall, *op. cit.* (8).

13. See, for example, J. Hadamard, *An Essay on the Psychology of Invention in the Mathematical Field* (Princeton Univ. Press, Princeton, 1949).

14. Although I was led to the thought of this section by reading Mayer, it was gratifying to find the same conception in the exploratory article by S. Lilley, "Social aspects of the history of Science," sect. vi, *Arch. intern. hist. sci.* **28**, 376 (1949).

15. This section is broadly due to the researches of Zilsel. See also Kelsen, *op. cit.* (10); E. V. Arnold, *Roman Stoicism* (Cambridge Univ. Press. Cambridge, 1911); and J. Needham's Hobhouse memorial lecture for 1950, *Human Law and the Laws of Nature in China and the West* (Oxford Univ. Press, London, 1951) from which the final quotation is taken (p. 42). Needham's studies are carried further in his article "The pat-

tern of nature-mysticism and empiricism in the philosophy of science: third century B.C. China, tenth century A.D. Arabia, and seventeenth century A.D. Europe" in the second volume of *Science, Medicine and History* (3). My remark about the organic self-causation views of Chinese thought are due, in part, to Derk Bodde "Harmony and Conflict in Chinese Philosophy," an essay in *Studies in Chinese Thought,* Arthur Wright, Ed., Memoir 75 of the American Anthropological Association (Chicago, 1953).

NOTES ABOUT THE CONTRIBUTORS

Philipp G. Frank

Dr. Frank received his Ph.D. from the University of Vienna, and taught from 1912 to 1938 at the University of Prague. Since 1940, he has been a faculty lecturer in physics and the philosophy of science at Harvard University, Cambridge, Massachusetts.

Gustav Bergmann

Dr. Bergmann, who received his Ph.D. in mathematics at the University of Vienna, has been connected with the State University of Iowa since 1939, and is at present professor of philosophy and psychology there. His primary interest is in the theory of knowledge, but he has done much work in the philosophy of science, particularly in the logic of psychology.

Edwin G. Boring

Dr. Boring was Director of the Harvard Psychological Laboratory, Cambridge, Massachusetts, for twenty-five years and at present is Edgar Pierce Professor of Psychology at Harvard University. His books on the history of experimental psychology and his writings on theoretical and systematic psychology are well known.

P. W. Bridgman

Dr. Bridgman was associated with Harvard University from the time of his entrance as an undergraduate in 1900 until his death in 1961. His principal scientific work was experimental, in the field of high pressure, and he was concerned with thermodynamics, and the critical analysis of the foundations of physics.

C. West Churchman

Dr. Churchman received his Ph.D. from the University of Pennsylvania in 1938 and has been professor of engineering administration at Case Institute of Technology. He is the author of several books on measurement of consumer interest, the theory of experimental inference and methods of making experimental in ferences, methods of inquiry, and phychologistics.

Robert S. Cohen

Dr. Cohen is associate professor of physics and chemistry at Boston University. During World War II he served on the scientific staff of the Columbia University Division of War Research and on the Communications Board of the U.S. Joint Chiefs of Staff.

Else Frenkel-Brunswik

Dr. Frenkel-Brunswik has done research in psychology at the University of Vienna where she received her Ph.D. in 1930, and more recently at the University of California in Berkeley, where she has been lecturer in psychology and associate research psychologist. In 1954–55 she served as a Fellow of the Center for Advanced Study in the Behavioral Sciences, Stanford, California.

Adolf Grünbaum

Dr. Grünbaum received his Ph.D. in philosophy from Yale and is now William Wilson Selfridge Professor of Philosophy at Lehigh University, Bethlehem, Pennsylvania, and, in 1956–57, was visiting research professor at the University of Minnesota Center for Philosophy of Science. He was the recipient of Lehigh University's Robinson Award in 1953 for outstanding service.

Henry Guerlac

Dr. Guerlac, professor of history of science, Cornell University, trained in biochemistry at Cornell and received his Ph.D. in European history at Harvard. A recent leave of absence was spent at the Institute for Advanced Study, Princeton, New Jersey.

Carl G. Hempel

Dr. Hempel, Stuart Professor of Philosophy at Princeton University, studied philosophy, mathematics, and physics at Goettingen, Heidelberg, Vienna, and Berlin (Ph.D. 1934). He has written articles in logic and philosophy of science and is the author of *Der Typusbegriff im Lichte der Neuen Logik* (with Paul Oppenheim) and *Fundamentals of Concept Formation in Empirical Science*.

Wolfgang Köhler

Dr. Köhler received his Ph.D. in psychology at Berlin in 1909, and was professor of psychology at Swarthmore College from 1935 to 1955. He has been visiting research professor of psychology at Dartmouth College since 1958. He is known for his work in perception, memory and the psychology of anthropoids other than man.

Alexandre Koyré

Dr. Koyré had been professor at the École Pratique des Hautes Etudes, Sorbonne, Paris, France, since 1930, and has been a visiting professor at Chicago, Johns Hopkins, and Wisconsin universities, and a member of the Institute for Advanced Study at Princeton.

R. Bruce Lindsay

Dr. Lindsay, Hazard Professor of Physics at Brown University since 1936, has been Dean of the Graduate School since 1954 and is also Director of the Ultrasonics Laboratory. Dr. Lindsay received his training at Brown University and the Massachusetts Institute of Technology, taking his Ph.D. in theoretical physics.

Warren S. McCulloch

Dr. McCulloch was educated at Yale, New York, and Columbia universities, and is now a staff member of the Research Laboratory of Electronics at Massachusetts Institute of Technology, where he conducts research on the central nervous system.

Henry Margenau

Dr. Margenau is Eugene Higgins Professor of Natural Philosophy and Physics at Yale University, where he received his Ph.D. in 1929. His special fields are atomic physics, nuclear physics, and the philosophy of physics. He is the author of several books in these fields.

Barrington Moore, Jr.

Dr. Moore is senior research fellow at the Russian Research Center of Harvard University and author of two well-known books: *Soviet Politics—The Dilemma of Power,* and *Terror and Progress —USSR.*

Nicolas Rashevsky

Dr. Rashevsky taught at Robert College, Istanbul, and the Russian University in Prague before serving ten years as a research physicist with the Westinghouse Electric and Manufacturing Corporation. Since 1935 he has been at the University of Chicago, where he is professor of mathematical biology.

Jerome Richfield

Dr. Richfield is associate professor of philosophy in the Bucknell University program of integrated studies. In recent years he has devoted himself to the philosophic problems in psychiatric theory. He has taught philosophy at the University of Cincinnati and also at Vassar College.

Richard Rudner

Dr. Rudner received his Ph.D. from the University of Pennsylvania and at present is with the department of philosophy, Michigan

State University. In addition to teaching the philosophy of science at Cornell, Washington University, Tufts, and Swarthmore, he is the author of several articles in the philosophy of science and other fields.

Michael Scriven

Michael Scriven, who was born in England, graduated from the Honours School of Mathematics at the University of Melbourne, and wrote his master's thesis on the limitations of symbolic logic. After two years of research at Oxford University, in philosophical psychology, he joined the faculty of the University of Minnesota where he now divides his time between the department of philosophy and the Minnesota Center for the Philosophy of Science.

Raymond J. Seeger

Dr. Seeger received his Ph.D. in mathematical physics from Yale. He taught physics for many years at the George Washington University and during World War II became interested in fluid dynamics, particularly high-speed phenomena in fundamental explosives research and in hyperballistics. He is now acting assistant director of the Mathematical, Physical, and Engineering Sciences Division of the National Science Foundation.

B. F. Skinner

Dr. Skinner received his Ph.D. from Harvard University, where he now is professor of psychology. He is author of several books including *Science and Human Behavior* and a utopian novel, *Walden Two*. He has contributed to the experimental analysis of behavior through work with rats and pigeons, and has recently extended his techniques to the human organism in the study of psychotic behavior.

INDEX

215